Special Boat Squadron

The MEDITERRANEAN

BY THE SAME AUTHOR

NON-FICTION
Zeebrugge, St George's Day, 1918
Coronel and Falkland
1918 – The Last Act
The Battle of the Atlantic
The Crucible of War: Western Desert 1941
The Crucible of War: Year of Alamein 1942
Churchill and the Generals

FICTION
The Edge of Battle

Special Boat Squadron

THE STORY OF THE SBS
IN THE MEDITERRANEAN

BARRIE PITT

C

CENTURY PUBLISHING
LONDON

First published in Great Britain in 1983
by Century Publishing Co. Ltd,
76 Old Compton Street, London W1V 5PA

ISBN 0 7126 0180 2

*Jacket photograph by Rick Jolly: Four-man patrol
waiting to go out by helicopter from HMS Fearless*

Photoset in North Wales by
Derek Doyle & Associates, Mold, Clwyd
Printed in Great Britain by
Butler & Tanner Ltd, Frome and London

To B Squadron
and especially
Ian and Stewart, Dick and David,
Reg and Lou, Jimmy and Pete,
and the brothers Bill and Harry.

AUTHOR'S NOTE

I have wanted for many years to write the story of the operations carried out in the Aegean by the men of the Special Boat Squadrons, and I must express my gratitude to Anthony Cheetham for creating the opportunity for me to do so. I must also, of course, express the same gratitude to all those who have helped me carry out the task.

The Rt. Hon. Earl Jellicoe D.S.O., M.C., Colonel D.G.C. Sutherland M.C., and Colonel J. Neilson Lapraik D.S.O., O.B.E., M.C., were all most helpful and indeed a very great deal of the primary material from which this narrative has been constructed comes from the collection of Operational Reports and personal accounts which Colonel Sutherland made available to me, as did several of the photographs. To Colonel C.A.H.M. Noble M.C., I must once again express my thanks for help given – this time somewhat coincidentally as he happened to be in possession of the diaries of the late Major Walter Milner-Barry at a most propitious moment, and he used his good offices to make them available to me – in which connection I would also like to express my gratitude to Sir Stuart Milner-Barry and his daughter.

Mrs. Norah Livingstone was kind enough to let me see her late husband's papers, thereby increasing the debt I owed both of them for hospitality extended to myself and my family many years ago, and I would like to thank her nephew, Captain J. James R.H.A. for his help in the matter.

Conversations held over the years with Stewart Macbeth, John Riley, Jack Nicholson, 'Tanky' Geary, Shaun O'Reilly, Jock Cunningham, Eric Lilley and David Clark have all contributed either to the narrative or the atmosphere of the tale told in the following pages, in which, of course, they all played significant parts; their memories of those days –

sometimes sad, often exciting, more often hilarious and never bitter – have remained in my mind to cheer me up whenever spirits are low.

I have received great encouragement while writing this book from many people. Lieutenant-Colonel 'Pug' Davis D.S.C. and Major 'Ram' Seager M.C. were both far more helpful to a complete stranger than ordinary courtesy would warrant, and perhaps in time the hopes we held for a detailed history of post-war S.B.S. operations will be realised; and both Sir John Verney and Eric Newby have added to the debts I already owe them for the pleasure their writings have given me over the years. I trust they will forgive me for not going into details of the raids in which they themselves participated, but I salve my conscience with the reflection that I could hardly improve upon the delightful accounts they have themselves given in their own books.

Finally I would like to thank Sarah Wallace for her help in the production of the book, Jane Caunt for once again typing my work, and Frances Mary Moore for drawing the maps in such detail and with such style.

CONTENTS

	PROLOGUE	1
1	EARLY DAYS 1940 – September '42	11
2	REORGANISATION September '42 – July '43	45
3	DODECANESE DISASTER July '43 – November '43	83
4	THE AEGEAN ISLAND RAIDS November '43 – August '44	123
5	TRIUMPH AND FRUSTRATION ON THE MAINLAND August '44 – April '45	161
	EPILOGUE	193
	CHRONOLOGY OF EVENTS	203
	NOTES	207
	INDEX	209

MAPS

The Mediterranean (*frontispiece*)	ii-iii
Crete	26
Rhodes	35
Crete, June 1943	71
The Dodecanese	95
The Aegean Islands	136-137
Simi	151
Greece	168
Istria and Dalmatia	184
Lake Comacchio	187

PROLOGUE

Some years after the war Mr. Churchill was asked which period for him had been the most anxious, and he answered without hesitation, 'September and October, 1942'. With the blessings of hindsight it is possible now to see that these months were indeed the turning-point of the war and that within a short time the balance would swing at last in favour of the Allies. But at that time the enormous battles around Stalingrad were in their early stages and the Pacific campaigns in Guadalcanal and New Guinea were showing little sign of resolution, while at the eastern end of the Mediterranean theatre, although Rommel's Panzerarmee Afrika had been halted before Alamein, and the holding battle of Alam Halfa had offered the hope that in General Montgomery the Eighth Army might at last be commanded by a 'Winning General', there was still no certainty that Rommel's army might not yet possess the power to drive through to the Nile and across the Sinai towards the vital oil-fields of the Persian Gulf – there perhaps to meet triumphant German armies pouring down through the Caucasus.

Perhaps the brightest hope for the Allies lay in the fact that agreement had at last been reached upon the joint Anglo-American invasion of North Africa, *Operation Torch*, and that fleets of merchant ships and their escorts were already congregating along America's eastern seaboard and in the British ports in north-east England and Northern Ireland. The strategic aim of the operation was to put Allied forces ashore between Casablanca and Algiers in such strength that they could reach the main Tunisian ports of Bizerta and Tunis before the enemy – whose Sicilian bases were less than 300 miles away. The Allied forces had to cross either 4,000 miles of ocean from America or 2,000 miles from Great Britain, and those that landed at Casablanca would then have another 1,200 miles to travel along a narrow and rudimentary road system.

Quite obviously, a hostile reception by the controlling forces in Morocco and Algeria would have a potentially disastrous effect upon both the landings themselves and the subsequent advance into Tunisia – and those controlling forces were French, traditionally well-disposed towards their fellow-republicans across the Atlantic, but not so well-disposed to their late Allies, the British, especially since the destruction of the French Fleet at Mers el Kebir in the wake of the French collapse of 1940.

How, in fact, would the French react when convoys containing both British and American troops arrived off their coastline, escorted by battleships of the Royal Navy which would undoubtedly open fire on the beaches unless firm guarantees of amicable reception had been arrived at beforehand?

It was a question which exercised many minds, and in the latter half of October a small party set out to try to discover the answer.

Bright moonlight flooded the scene, silvering the wave-tops and silhouetting the North African coastline against the dark, velvet sky, the pyramidal snout of Cape Tenez thrusting up into the night away to the west, Mount Tourira to the east. Straight ahead, the white guiding-light punctured the shadows above the landing-bay.

However busy the submarine crew might be, there was for the moment nothing to occupy the three British commandos waiting among the Americans on the conning-tower and casing, except to reflect upon the intriguing possibilities of the immediate future and the curious events of the immediate past – so curious indeed that they made the fact that H.M. Submarine *Seraph* was on her final approach to an enemy coastline in conditions of almost spectacular visibility somehow not so disconcerting as it otherwise would have been. It did seem quite incredible, however, that although they could see every detail for miles around, no one – at least, no one hostile – could apparently see them.

No one hostile had seen them yesterday, either, as they raced along on a calm blue surface under clear skies, with the snow-capped Sierra Nevadas fading away to port and Gibraltar dropping further and further astern. Speed and timing were apparently so important on this operation that they overrode the natural fears of *Seraph*'s commander, Lieutenant Bill Jewell, who at one point had been heard to mutter that if this sort of procedure was often to be followed, he might just as well have joined the Fleet Air Arm and had done with it. But then, he was one of those eccentrics who never felt happy without thirty fathoms of sea-water above him.

The shore crept closer, the men on the casing and conning-tower muttered among themselves, going over everything again in their minds, assuring themselves that the folboats were checked, the papers and gear assembled and packed, the weapons cleaned and the magazines filled. Soon they would be away and on their own.

The submarine slowed, and stopped – and with the loss of forward motion the true weather and water conditions could be gauged. The lumpy, untidy swell which had seemed fairly innocuous while they were moving through it revealed itself as a quite considerable slop which rose and fell a couple of feet, and the first folboat over the side yawed well away before the sailors at the bow and stern lines could nurse it back into position. The first commando edged his way into the front cockpit, to be followed into the rear cockpit with admirable and unexpected ease by the American colonel, whose only previous experience of such an uncomfortable and wayward craft had been a brief experimental run the previous night.

Quickly, the folboat pulled away and the two men waited while the second pair – another commando officer with a brigadier-general as his cargo – copied their manoeuvre and quickly joined them. Together they watched the endeavours of the third pair – the senior pair, for Captain Courtney was the commando in charge of the landing operation and his cargo was a major-general, no less. Ironically, minor disaster struck. The folboat yawed widely as it entered the water, came back too quickly and just as 'Gruff' Courtney was lowering himself into it, it was trapped under the casing overhang and overturned, the wood of the middle starboard rib and the forward deck strut broken.

Apprehensively, the men in the two launched boats watched and waited. They saw Courtney climb back aboard the submarine, a hasty discussion take place among the men still clustered on the casing, then the fourth folboat go over the side with its original No. 1 – a United States Navy captain – in the front cockpit, and then the major-general clamber down into the rear position. The three folboats afloat assembled, turned, and in arrowhead formation, moved in towards the coast and the guiding-light above it.

In the leading boat were Captain R.P. Livingstone and Colonel Julius C. Holmes, and it was their responsibility to go first into the beach and ensure that neither accidental danger nor betrayal awaited the party; Livingstone could judge the landing conditions, and Holmes knew the men who should be meeting them. Some 1,200 yards off the surf line, this pair therefore moved ahead on their own, stopping frequently to examine the shore through night-glasses, making better time through calmer water once they had reached the lee of the land and escaped the wind sweeping down the Wadi Messelmoun. Silently they rode through the last waves, and with a slight hiss the canvas hull slid up the sand amid the soft wash of ripples. The men tore open their canvas aprons and leaped out, anxious to get away from the open, moonlit beach and into the shadows at the foot of the bluff – and as they dragged the boat from the water, a dark figure detached itself from the tree-shadows to their left and crunched openly across the sand towards them.

Livingstone brought up his Tommy-gun, Holmes snatched at his pistol, but then walked forward with a word of greeting – the figure was a friend, to be joined immediately by more friends whose relief and amiability were such that Livingstone had eventually to break up a back-slapping convention in order to get the boat carried the rest of the way into the shadows and see that elementary precautions against surprise were taken. He then flashed a signal to the offshore folboats and soon could see the first two with brigadier and major-general aboard moving inshore, then beyond them a third shape, recognisably that of a quickly repaired folboat bearing the sodden and somewhat peevish Courtney with the remaining member of the American team.

Very quickly all were ashore, and while spare hands lifted the craft and gear into the shadows, the commandos prowled along the edge of the bay and the Americans held a quick and whispered conference with their hosts. Eventually the tall form of Major-General Mark Clark detached itself from the group and walked towards Courtney.

There was far too much to be discussed, he said, for there to be any possibility of a return to the submarine before morning. The whole party must therefore go up to the villa above where they could spend the next day, and *Seraph* must return for them all the following night – a situation which had to some extent been foreseen and posed no difficulties. There was a brief but guarded radio conversation between Courtney and Bill Jewell, a flurry of activity at the foot of the bluff, and then a panting struggle up a steep, narrow and crumbling path, the commandos and the American officers carrying the guns and the folboats, the welcoming party carrying the gear, the spare magazines, the inevitable American briefcases.

'*C'est vous Rene?*'

'*C'est moi.*'

The path reached a level, gravelled area shadowed by a huge, gnarled olive tree beyond which stretched a white wall with a green wooden gate through which the party made its way, the folboats now weighing a ton each. As the gate closed behind them, they found themselves in the villa courtyard – exactly, Livingstone was to write later, as he had imagined a Moorish interior to be:

... a long rather narrow courtyard with palms growing down the middle enclosed on three sides by the white house and its wings, and on the fourth by the curtain wall in which the gate was set. Narrow red-tiled verandas with pent-house roofs carried on green-painted posts ran along each side. It was a New Testament scene, a place of brightness and black shadow. The palms rattled their dry leaves and the scalloped edges of the pan-tiled roof were black against the deep-blue sky, where the stars sparkled in more-than-Oriental splendour, as the boats were hurried in and kit was dumped in the shadows.

It must have made a curious sight, the tall, leisurely Americans, with their slow speech, the quick-moving Frenchmen conducting staccato arguments in low voices as they flitted about, and the three silent, shaggy Commandos, tommy-guns sticking up over their shoulders, standing aside, suspicious and watchful.[1]

For Livingstone, Courtney and Foot, there was now little to do except wait and keep watch until the time came to organise departure for their passengers and themselves, and safe rendezvous with the submarine. They had no part to play in the political and strategic discussions which now began and were to occupy the Americans and the Frenchmen for the rest of the night and all the following morning: the pledges of support by the French for a large-scale Allied landing along the North African coastline, the details of garrisons or naval contingents who might or might not contend the landings in support of the Vichy Government, in loyalty to the old Marshal Pétain or even stronger loyalty to their own Admiral Darlan. These were the business of Generals Clark and Lemnitzer and of the shipping and supply advisers and the State Department officer whom they had brought with them.

So in the meantime, the commandos slept, their clothes spread out to dry on the floor of a spacious room allotted to them, their heads on their haversacks. With the resilience of young professionals, they sloughed off the discomforts and perils of the immediate past, gave only technical consideration to probable future complications and lived in what for the moment promised to be a most acceptable present – an impression heightened when they were awakened on the beautiful sunny morning which followed the landing with large cups of excellent coffee and rolls of rye bread.

Their time of leisure and relaxation was to continue, they were informed, for the rest of the day. They could not, alas, be allowed to go sight-seeing or even to exercise, for it was essential that their presence remained undiscovered; instead they must stay in their room until the time came for departure, not even drawing back the shutters, let alone sunning themselves on the balcony. The French were undoubtedly tense and somewhat uneasy, but their precautions were not unreasonable – as was demonstrated soon afterwards by the passage overhead of an He. 111 of the Axis Control Commission.

The day therefore passed quietly for the British, while below them in the living-rooms, agreement was reached between the French and the Americans on tactical moves to be made immediately the Anglo-American fleets arrived off the North African coasts and on who would occupy each particular niche in the subsequent command structure. And agreement was also reached that as soon as it was dark, at about eight o'clock, the whole party would make their way down to the beach, contact the submarine and depart.

It was therefore a moment of some drama when just before half-past seven the telephone rang with the news that the unusual activity at the villa had been reported to the police, who were even then on their way to investigate.

The next few minutes were of hectic and not always controlled confusion. The French with the exception of the owner of the villa and the caretaker flung briefcases into cars and disappeared rapidly in the direction of Algiers, one of the commandos, Lieutenant Foot, raced down to the beach and flashed a warning to the submarine of imminent danger, while the other two, assisted by Colonels Holmes and Hamblen, began disinterring the folboats from their hiding-places; but time was judged too short and the light too strong as yet for a disembarkation, so the boats were slung back into the room and the door locked.

It was obvious that the party must hide. The five U.S. officers and the three British commandos were hurried down into a dark, cobwebby pit which had once been a wine-cellar (but was now, unfortunately, empty), the trap door slammed and the two Frenchmen and two civilian Americans – Robert Murphy and his assistant Ridgeway Knight, who were both accredited representatives of the State Department in North Africa – awaited the arrival of the French police. They clanked bottles, sang in somewhat maudlin tones, and when the police did eventually arrive, explained that they had been holding a very jolly party and that there were girls upstairs whose presence, if it became known, would prove embarrassing to the American consuls. Surely there was no need for further investigation?

The police were sullen and suspicious, but in the end, having tramped through the lower rooms and over the top of the wine-cellar for what seemed hours to those penned below, departed, muttering dire warnings of retribution, reports and probable return.

The soldiers emerged with considerable relief. One of the

more immediate worries in the cellar for both Courtney and
Livingstone had been that when they had taken station on
each side of the ladder with General Clark between them, the
general had insisted that in the case of discovery they must, if
all else failed, shoot their way out. His own position, he
announced, would be in the lead – an admirable attitude to
take, but one somewhat discounted by the fact that for a long
time he had fiddled with the loaded carbine he had been
given, clicking the mechanism up and down and wondering
audibly to himself how the God-damned thing worked.

Eventually, someone told him to put it down 'in tones no one
should use to a general', but now out in the open again, it
quickly became evident that Monsieur Teissier's nerve had
been severely shaken and that he could not wait for them to
leave his premises. In short order the folboats, radio, weapons,
papers and assorted gear were collected and manhandled down
to the beach – where the party found themselves faced with
another seemingly intractable problem. During their time in
the cellar, the wind had risen, and now the surf was curling
thunderously down on to the steep-to beach with such force as
to daunt even the most well-trained and experienced canoeist.
The seas beyond were running high, and the submarine was
waiting four miles out.

Courtney set up the radio and asked Jewell to come in
closer, and soon afterwards Livingstone, using one of the new
infra-red devices, picked up *Seraph* as she made her way in.
Then he and General Clark stripped to their underclothing
and attempted the first re-embarkation, but it quickly became
evident that conditions were too rough. Though they managed
to get aboard and through the first surf, they were then caught
by a huge wave which caused the folboat to rear up almost
vertically and overturn, thus losing General Clark his trousers
and a money-belt which contained several hundred dollars in
gold – and convincing Courtney that they must wait until
conditions improved.

It was a long, cold, nerve-stretching wait. The Frenchmen
were insistent that the party get away from the area (and so
obviously apprehensive about the situation that General Clark
used their fears to cajole dry clothes, food and wine from
them), but no other solution than sitting and waiting for the
wind to drop was practicable. There was no way of hiring a

fishing-boat even with gold dollars (for other members beside the general had them sewn into their clothing), and false papers and a car ride into Spanish Morocco were judged too risky – but as the night wore on, the wind dropped, and although the surf remained high, Courtney, prowling up and down the waterline, discovered a place where, he proclaimed, there showed an occasional slight break.

No one else could see it, but time was passing inexorably, so at about four o'clock on that cold, dark morning, the whole party stripped to their underclothes and carried the first folboat out through the initial line of surf. Once through it, General Clark and the American naval Captain Wright scrambled into the cockpits, while the rest of the party lifted the boat up and down to stabilise it as the surf rushed underneath, finally heaving it monstrously forward as general and captain paddled furiously out into clear water. Cold, dripping, but enormously relieved, the remainder watched them disappear into the darkness.

Lieutenant Foot and Colonel Hamblen tried next and almost immediately came to grief; while they recovered, Courtney tried with Brigadier-General Lemnitzer, but they too were quickly overturned and swamped. With no alternative, they all tried again ... and again ... and again, and in the end all four folboats were following each other out towards the waiting submarine, the occupants wet through and nearing exhaustion, the beach behind littered with discarded clothing, mess-tins, rations – and several copies of important papers which the French and the two American diplomats were hastily gathering together.

As Captain Livingstone at last scrambled up the conning-tower, he glanced back to see two pairs of headlights converging along the road on each side of the villa, where they stopped: the police had arrived, and Robert Murphy would have to tell his tale and exert his charm all over again.

In this, as it happened, he was successful, and also in the concealment of the clothing and kit and, incredibly, in the recovery of most of the lost gold – much to the relief of Brigadier-General Lemnitzer, who, according to Livingstone, spent much of the following day gloomily speculating upon what a certain Mr. Morgenthau of the U.S. Treasury would have to say about the loss of yet another $20,000 by the irresponsible military.

But this was a matter of no import to the commandos. They had done what had been asked of them, safely delivering to their rendezvous on an enemy coast a party of high-ranking American officers and bringing them back again off a death-trap of a beach. The following day, a Catalina flying boat flew out and settled on the water a few hundred yards from the surfaced *Seraph*, and once again Courtney, Foot and Livingstone ferried the Americans across the intervening water, bidding them all goodbye with cordial farewells and mutual promises of future meetings.

No such meetings took place, in fact, for many months, even years; but none of the Americans – and certainly not General Clark or Brigadier-General Lemnitzer – ever forgot their first meeting with the men of the Special Boat Section.

ONE

Early Days

The landing of the American generals and their staff officers
on the North African coast at the end of 1942 was certainly the
most prestigious operation carried out by the men of the
Special Boat Section to that date, but it was by no means the
first. Accepted lore is that this occurred on the night of June
22nd, 1941, when Lieutenant 'Tug' Wilson and Marine
'Wally' Hughes landed on the west coast of Italy, placed
explosives under a main railway-line where it ran through a
tunnel, and were back aboard the submarine, folboat safely
stowed and some ham sandwiches devoured when the officer
was called to the bridge. He arrived in time to see through
night-glasses a long train entering the tunnel, a spectacular
white flash a few seconds later, followed by the sounds of a
massive explosion booming across the sea towards them.

The episode provided the first justification of weeks of
argument and persuasion by two or three folboat enthusiasts,
followed by months of hard training.

The idea of using canoes in warlike activity had apparently
first occurred to Roger Courtney – brother of the Gruff
Courtney who had commanded the operation just described –
shortly after Dunkirk. The evacuation had so shaken military
convention that such unorthodox formations as 'Independent
Companies' and 'Commandos' were not only allowed to exist,
but positively encouraged to do so. In those heady, far-off days
of the summer of 1940, Whitehall had been besieged by men
who had tramped across deserts, descended to claustrophobic

depths in caves, lived on berries and snakes in Africa or – as in Courtney's case – canoed down the White Nile during intervals between big game hunting, all of them convinced that in their own particular speciality lay an effective solution to the problem of how to strike back at Hitler's Germany.

Courtney was at the time a subaltern in No.8 Commando, recently formed by Lieutenant-Colonel Robert Laycock, an ex-Royal Horse Guards officer with a marked sense of humour, and Courtney was encouraged in his enthusiasms to such effect that during the following months some twenty officers and men, of whom Wilson and Hughes were among the most enthusiastic, spent many long, cold and exhausting hours learning to manage their wayward craft in the stormy waters around the rock-bound island of Arran. Their training also encompassed use of every weapon left in the British armoury after the débâcle of Dunkirk plus those which President Roosevelt had been able to prise from his own somewhat reluctant service quartermasters, and some specialist training in demolitions.

As a result of this latter activity, six of them found themselves somewhat unexpectedly attached to No.12 Commando during the first raid on the Lofoten Islands in November, 1940. They landed and placed most of their explosive successfully, and one of them at least achieved a certain modest distinction. Lance-Corporal Webb, laden with explosives and with both hands full, rounded a corner to find himself faced by three German soldiers, apparently hesitant upon their own immediate course of action despite the sounds of battle raging not far off.

Quick thinking on Webb's part saved the situation and probably his own life. Quoting instantaneously from an apochryphal Battle of Britain story the only two words of German he knew, he shouted '*Achtung, Schpitfeuer!*' at the top of his voice, thus causing the three Germans to drop their rifles and surrender. He experienced a certain amount of difficulty upon his return to base in persuading sceptical audiences of the truth of his report, but he certainly brought in three prisoners to support it.

In the meantime, all the training taking place along the west coast of Scotland began to take shape and specific aim, for at the turn of the year, 'Wavell's Thirty Thousand' were engaged in sweeping the Italian Tenth Army out of Cyrenaica as though with a twenty-mile-wide broom, and visions of a North African coast free of Axis presence by Easter 1941 were delighting minds in both Whitehall and Cairo. Thus, perhaps an assault on the Italian mainland or at least on Sicily might not be far off – in which case possession of the offshore island of Pantellaria would be an advantage, its capture and occupation surely just the kind of exercise these newly-formed assault units would welcome.

As it happened, events in Greece and the sudden appearance of German panzer units in Tripolitania put an abrupt end to such dreams; but were to raise instead tempting targets for specialist forces elsewhere – and among those targets the Dodecanese island of Rhodes figured prominently. In response to requests made by General Wavell, Nos. 7, 8 and 11 Commandos, banded together as 'Layforce' under Brigadier Laycock, left Scotland on January 31st, 1941, and packed deep into the bowels of one of the convoy ships were the folboats of the Boat Section.

They arrived in the Suez area around the middle of March and trained assiduously on the waters of the Bitter Lakes for the Rhodes operation, though it was to be a long time before any of them were to land on that rocky and ruin-studded island. In the reverses suffered by the British once *Generalfeldmarschall* List's men reached Athens and the Peloponnese, many of Layforce's assault craft were wrecked and the original purpose for the Commandos' presence in the Middle East was forgotten in the press of events. Their continued existence as anything but a pool of reinforcement for more orthodox formations was called into question, and the force began inevitably to disintegrate.

Some men joined battalions of their original regiments already in the theatre; others were posted as reinforcements to units decimated in the recent fighting; some were grouped into a newly established Middle East Commando (for Mr. Churchill issued a broadsheet to the effect that the Commando idea was not to shrivel and die in the theatre for lack of immediate employment); some submitted to the blandishments of a tall subaltern in the Scots Guards to help form a 'Private Army' whose function would be to raid enemy lines of communication and supply miles behind the front positions in the desert. And Roger Courtney, who could not bear to be idle and anyway had no intention of seeing his precious folboats and their crews left unused or incorporated into some other, probably unsympathetic organisation, sought out and obtained an interview with Admiral Maund, Director of Combined Operations in Alexandria.

The admiral proved most open-minded and eager to help. Submarines under his command were constantly cruising off enemy coastlines in pursuit of hostile shipping, and there was no reason why they should not occasionally take on board one or two army experts who could carry their depredations deeper into enemy ports and harbours than the submarines themselves could venture, or even on to the enemy coastline itself. Thus it came about in mid-1941 that Courtney, Wilson, Hughes and the other stalwarts who had laboured with them in Scottish waters, found themselves installed aboard H.M.S. *Medway*, the depot ship for the 1st Submarine Flotilla.

They were quickly engaged upon a variety of tasks. On the Albanian and Cretan coasts they landed agents – sinister, rather seedy-looking characters who tended to complain in various Mediterranean approximations to the British tongue of wet trousers and even wetter shoes as they set off on their undoubtedly dangerous missions inland. Some of the S.B.S. men gained experience of life aboard submarines by enlisting as extra machine-gunners and in due course one of these, Corporal Booth, was to shoot down the gun-crew of a German supply ship when the captain of H.M. Submarine *Torbay* – perhaps mistakenly for his quarry was armed with a heavy gun amidships – decided to attack it on the surface. Fortunately the enemy gun had two misfires.

> I opened fire on the men who were attempting to man the forward gun and had the satisfaction of wiping them out. I then cleared the gun amidships. By this time our 4″ had opened fire and hit the lower part of the bridge. I then noticed a party of men running aft to man the after M.G. I opened fire and cleared the crew. This gun did not fire. By this time our 4″ gun crew had set the supply ship on fire and it evidently carried petrol as there were terrific flames. I noticed a man on the bridge whom I took to be the commander and I opened fire and removed him immediately. The sub. then dived and a few minutes later there were several explosions caused by the supply ship going up.

The patrol was carried out as usual after this.[1]

But the most successful operations were still those of the type carried out by Lieutenant Wilson and Marine Hughes. After their first spectacular success, the same two tried but failed to blow up a railway tunnel on the west coast of Italy and then, undaunted by the experience of zigzagging their folboat out into the night through a hail of rifle and Breda fire, they tried again between Ancona and Senigallia. After a long paddle in and an even longer walk carrying weapons and explosive across to the main Brindisi-Milan railway-line, they successfully placed a complicated series of charges between the sleepers – a task prolonged by the continual passage of trains whose passengers never had the slightest inkling of how fortunate they had been.

But at last the job was done and Wilson and Hughes withdrew – both relieved and disappointed by the fact that the night's traffic seemed to be at an end. They were safely back aboard H.M. Submarine *Truant* when the slow passage of a train towards the danger-spot was reported, then the boom of an explosion came echoing across the water as a fourteen-carriage Pullman blew up with a serious loss of life and the destruction not only of the train but of a satisfactory length of the track. It was many days before the wreckage was cleared away, by which time Wilson was on his way back to base with new ideas bubbling in his fertile mind.

Railways would soon, he reasoned, despite their exceptional vulnerability along the Italian coastlines, receive increasingly adequate defences (in itself a dispersion of enemy forces to justify his attacks) but shipping would be for the moment equally vulnerable, especially in harbour. A method of attack could be and soon was devised, though perhaps mid-December, even in the Mediterranean, was not the best time to try it out. A few days before Christmas, 1941, Lieutenant Wilson, clad in the heaviest woollen 'Long Johns' the quartermaster could obtain and liberally coated with Vaseline, slipped over the side of his folboat and, pushing a Limpet mine supported on netting wrapped around a rubber tyre, swam in towards an Italian destroyer moored alongside the pier in Navarino Bay.

He was seriously hampered by the fact that if he swam too

energetically he stirred up a spectacular phosphorescence and that if he did not he stood in danger of rapid hypothermia, so perhaps fortunately for him the crucial decision lay with Marine Hughes. His superior had gone overboard attached to a line, and, seeing no point in losing an excellent officer from the service – and a friend – Hughes began pulling it in after what he considered a reasonable lapse of time. Eventually, the marine dragged a benumbed Lieutenant Wilson up and into the front cockpit of the folboat and, despite the unusual hazard presented by the machine-gun rattling of his superior's teeth, successfully organised their return to the attendant submarine.

'I feel certain I would have been successful had I been able to withstand the cold,' reported Wilson, indicating for the first time a danger which would threaten S.B.S. men at every development and in almost every theatre in which they were to be employed.

By now the Special Boat Section had attained an official name together with the rudiments of administrative existence, signalised by the appearance of truck-loads of forms to be filled in, and even a unit stamp – though as this had been made in the local Arab saddlery, it was the cause of some puzzlement. What exactly were the functions, a myopic pay-clerk was heard plaintively enquiring, of the Special Boot Section?

But with this respectability came a wider clientèle for the section's services. In the early part of October 1941, six officers and fifty-three men from the old No.11 Commando congregated in the Canal Zone under command of the young Lieutenant-Colonel Geoffrey Keyes, elder son of Admiral Keyes, the first Director of Combined Operations. Their objective was to land on the coast of Cyrenaica, then make their way inland to attack the Italian headquarters at Cyrene and the Intelligence centre at Appollonia, wreck Axis communications further inland and then to attack the German headquarters at Beda Littoria. It was also intended that they should investigate a small villa to the west of the German headquarters which was believed to be the personal residence of General Rommel, and despite the fact that this objective was abandoned early in the operation, such was the Press reaction when eventually the story of the raid came out that it has been known ever since as 'The Rommel Raid' – or even 'The Raid to "Get" Rommel'.

The part to be played by the men of the S.B.S. was small but vital. Upon arrival off the selected stretch of coastline, folboats were to be slipped from the two submarines (H.M. Submarines *Torbay* and *Talisman*) and two pairs of S.B.S. men go ashore, make certain that the beaches were not occupied by enemy ambuscade, then signal in the main force whose rubber boats the S.B.S. would help conceal.

This they did with commendable success despite the appalling weather conditions, which were such that it took seven hours instead of ninety minutes to land the commandos from *Torbay*, while those from *Talisman* never reached the beaches at all, several being swept off the submarine's combing and never seen again. In spite of this, Lieutenants Ingles and Allott and their No.2s. carried out their part of the operation, hid the commandos' rubber boats, bade Keyes and his men farewell and good luck, and returned to the *Torbay*.

They then waited in various degrees of apprehension for three days and nights, closing the beach again just after nightfall on November 18th (the opening day of *Operation Crusader*, the Eighth Army offensive destined to relieve Tobruk and throw Rommel back into Tripolitania – but not, alas, for the last time). According to Lieutenant Tommy Langton,

> We were relieved to see the arranged signal from the beach, but it was much too rough to launch a folboat. The Captain having decided to send Lt. Ingles and Cpl. Severn in on a spare rubber, this was attempted but the boat was washed adrift by the swell before the crew could board it, so the attempt was abandoned. Later the party ashore reported that they had found the boat with the water and food which had been loaded therein. They also reported that there were twenty-two of them there but they did not know what had happened to the others, or to the rubber boats which had been left on the beaches. They declined the Captain's suggestions that they should swim off at dawn, so we put to sea again.
>
> We closed the beach very soon after dark the next night, and the sea was considerably calmer, though a long swell was running in from the N.W. *i.e.*, straight on to the beach. We were dismayed to see no signals from the beach this time [*Author's note.* The men ashore had been discovered and attacked by Italian troops, so

some had already been captured and the rest were dispersed] so, after waiting some time, the Captain decided to send myself and Cpl. Feeberry in to reconnoitre. Launching the folboat from the planes was again very difficult, and by the time we got away we had shipped a lot of water. I had hoped to approach the beach slowly and turn the boat around to face seawards before getting out. But the long swell prevented this and – in spite of our combined 28 stone – we rode into the beach on the crest of a wave like a couple of mermaids.

The beach was deserted, and after emptying the boat we walked off along the beach towards a light which had appeared on the hillside. This light was the correct colour, but not giving the correct signals, so I was most suspicious of it. After going a little way I thought I saw a movement inland, so we crept towards it but saw nothing further. However, we both heard a shout soon afterwards, and since we were by then some distance from our boat and liable to be cut off, I decided to return to it and wait.[2]

No further signs of life appeared during the next ten minutes, so, mystified but still intent on finding any of the raid's survivors if they were present, Langton and Feeberry launched their folboat out through the line of breakers and paddled along parallel to the shore towards the light. Abreast of it, Langton flashed his own white torch, heard in reply a shout but saw no answering signal, and was pondering the situation when a broadside wave filled the boat and they were forced, willy-nilly, to run in again. More trouble befell them just before they grounded and they were upturned, in the resulting confusion temporarily losing one of their Tommy-guns and permanently – and potentially disastrously – one of their paddles.

No rational explanation of the events of the next hour has ever been forthcoming. Leaving one to guard the folboat, Langton and Feeberry took turns to search for the missing paddle, between them covering the whole length of the beach – and all the time they were conscious of the fact that several cigarette-smokers were grouped around the still-shining light just above the beach, occasional murmured spurts of conversation came to them above the break of the surf, yet no one approached. Deciding that no survivor from such a raid as Keyes's men had carried out would risk discovery by smoking in the open on a dark night, Langton decided to return to the submarine – a journey out through the surf and half a mile beyond with one paddle that was only made possible by Corporal Feeberry's immense physical strength and determination. They shipped a great deal of water during the trip and were in such immediate danger of sinking that, once the fore and aft lines had been made fast, they both slid over the side and scrambled up on the submarine through breaking waves – and the folboat's wooden struts snapped under the weight of water when the boat was bodily lifted from the sea.

The following morning, they watched through the periscope as Italian and later German troops searched the beach, finding nothing of value or significance, for the commandos had destroyed all evidence of their presence before dispersing. Only two of these reached the safety of their own lines – one of them being Colonel Laycock himself, who had accompanied Keyes as an 'observer'. Keyes himself had been killed during the attack on the German headquarters and was later awarded a posthumous Victoria Cross.

Though the operation as a whole had not been a great success, the attached S.B.S. party had fulfilled their role efficiently, gained further experience and had the vital lesson again driven home that in the event of capsize, the last thing you let go of is your paddle.

During the months immediately after the 'Rommel Raid', the affairs of S.B.S. – from an historian's point of view – began to assume the characteristics of a loosely tangled ball of string. This was partly due to the expanding nature of the activities they undertook as their reputation grew, and partly to the more serious nature of the conflict in the Middle East as on the one hand Rommel's Panzergruppe took over from Graziani and then Bastico's Italian troops, while on the other Auchinleck's Eighth Army replaced Wavell's XIII Corps. The influx of new faces into the S.B.S. messes and canteens and the departure of some of the older ones was another complicating factor.

Roger Courtney's health had shown signs of breaking down during November, so he went home (where he very quickly gathered around him the nucleus of what was to become the 2nd S.B.S. which eventually went to the Far East) and his place was briefly taken by Captain Mike Kealy, who not long afterwards also went back to the U.K. Tug Wilson went away on what was believed to be a temporary detachment from which he did not, in fact, return to the S.B.S. (though Wally Hughes did), and one or two of the 'other ranks' were recommended for commissions and departed on the necessary re-assignment courses.

Their places were quickly taken, mostly by officers and men who had been in Layforce and kept themselves abreast of the activities of ex-comrades. Among them were Lieutenants David Sutherland and Eric Newby, both originally from the Black Watch, and Captains 'Tramp' Allott, Duncan and Grant-Watson from less artistically distinguished formations. As for the No.2s. – variously referred to as 'half-portions' or 'muckers' – these now included such stalwarts as Corporals Riley, Barr, Pomford and Booth, plus such a mixture of Guardsmen, marines, sappers, gunners, riflemen and privates as to cause confusion throughout the echelons of the Pay Corps and make any form of ceremonial parade an impossibility.

Not that there was time for such martial theatricality, for these men and their folboats were now continuously engaged upon a variety of missions. Hardly a submarine of the 1st Flotilla left Alexandria without one or more pairs aboard; agents were dropped or picked up; beaches were reconnoitred for possible large-scale landings; Greek caiques or Italian trawlers, their owners confidently assuming that their craft were snugly secure in safe harbour, were blown up if they were actively hostile, or had their engines ruined with sand in the oil or sugar in the petrol if only potentially so. And to the extent that the *Kriegsmarine* became increasingly annoyed, the Royal Navy regarded these small bands of 'licensed brigands' with increasing favour, however unkempt their appearance, the submarine crews taking them to their collective hearts to such an extent that rum was on occasion shared with them in ceremonial 'sippers' after normal operations, or even, after some particularly spectacular success, 'gulpers'.

But besides the navy, the military, and in particular one newly born but rapidly growing formation, was also taking an interest in the Special Boat Section. The 'Private Army' set up by the tall Scots Guards subaltern had blossomed remarkably in the desert scene, and by the end of 1941 David Stirling commanded a force of over 100 trained operatives, who rampaged through the rear areas of the Panzerarmee, wrecked vehicle parks, blew up Luftwaffe bombers and fighters, shot up headquarters from corps to company level, and strained the nerves of the Italian supply services stretching back to Tripoli.

And with the arrival of the Eighth Army on the Gulf of Sirte in January, 1942, the thought crossed Stirling's mind that, without Benghazi, Rommel must now bring the bulk of his supplies through the port of Buerat some 300 miles further west, thus providing a different category of target. Airfields, viaducts, barracks or road traffic he and his men knew how to deal with, but a walk around the still-smoking harbour of Benghazi convinced him that he needed another form of expertise if his organisation was to wreak satisfactory mayhem in this new area. So in mid-January Captain Duncan and Corporal Barr packed their folboat into a three-ton lorry and accompanied it – and thirty mixed personnel from both the Long Range Desert Group and Stirling's Special Air Service – through acres of sand seas and across far too many rocky, steep-sided ravines towards the outskirts of Buerat.

Not all that surprisingly, the folboat proved too fragile for such ragged overland travel which reduced it to a useless bundle of rubberised canvas and wood; but Duncan and Barr were quite content to join in the land operations, and between them they placed charges on twenty-three diesel trucks of which eighteen proved to be petrol-carriers, and also blew up the wireless station and mast, thus demonstrating – perhaps a little too convincingly – the ability of S.B.S. personnel to operate just as well on land as on sea.

This had immediate results, for two months later, after Rommel had initiated the fourth round of the Benghazi Handicap and pushed the Eighth Army back to Gazala, Stirling launched another party at Benghazi itself, this time containing a larger S.B.S. contingent. That there was still a great deal to be learned about the techniques of both navigation and logistics for such an operation became startlingly clear, and Tramp Allott was scathing on the subject:

OPERATION 1.
On the night of 20/21st March two trucks of L.R.D.G. took

parties from S.A.S. Brigade L Detachment and S.B.S. to raid BERCA AERODROME. S.B.S. target was BERCA MAIN. Party consisted of Captain ALLOTT, Cpl. POMFORD, Cpl. SINCLAIR and Lieut. ALSTON. Party was scheduled to arrive Half a mile EAST of railway running NORTH and SOUTH through BERCA at 2330 hours 20th March. Owing to the bad going and aerial activity on the 20th, the trucks did not arrive until 0110 hours 21st. It was reported by the navigator that the position of patrol was one mile EAST of railway and the course to the railway was 270°. The party set out at 0115 hours on that bearing and after marching four miles failed to find the railway. Lieut. ALSTON who was guide to the party reported that the trucks were out of position and that we were five miles SOUTH of correct position and at least seven miles EAST of the railway. Our orders were to return to the truck by 0330 hours 21st, therefore we returned to R.V. and arrived at 0325 hours. It was later found that truck was 7 miles EAST of railway and 3 miles SOUTH of correct position. It would have been impossible to have proceeded to aerodrome and completed task before light as there is no cover in that area.

Captain
Special Boat Section

OPERATION 2.

On the night of 28th/29th March, S.A.S. and S.B.S. proceeded to BENGHAZI. At 2300 hours 28th the party consisting of S.A.S. Brigade, L Det. Major Stirling – Lieut. Alston (to act as guide) and two corporals. S.B.S. Captain Allott – Cpl. Sinclair, Cpl. Pomford. Proceeded on the south road to BENGHAZI via REGIMA BENINA starting on the road 5 miles east of REGIMA. Having entered BENGHAZI from the south the party arrived on the west side of the outer mole. Captain ALLOTT and Cpl. SINCLAIR started to assemble the boat. They were detected by an Italian and proceeded 100 yards further west and started again to assemble the boat. It was found that the No.1 rib was broken, this was mended. Previously to this the bow and stern posts had been broken and had been mended with very limited stores. Owing to this damage and the distortion of the skin from heat and severe bumping whilst en route across the desert it was found impossible to assemble the boat. At about 0215 hours 29th it was decided to abandon the operation and the party proceeded by the NORTH road out of BENGHAZI. Nothing was left that could possibly show that we had been in BENGHAZI.

LESSON LEARNT. It would seem from this that a folboat is not suitable for use with L.R.D.G. unless a special container is devised, owing to the very severe conditions of the journey.

Captain Allott and Cpl. Sinclair undertook to perform this operation at the last moment as Lieut. Sutherland and Sgt. Moss were wounded on the way to BENGHAZI by their car striking a mine.

Captain
Special Boat Section.[3]

The operations as a whole could not be judged a success by anyone's standards; indeed, Benghazi harbour was always to remain a scene of frustration for raiding parties. Two months later David Stirling took another party into the port, this time consisting entirely of his own men and taking inflatable rubber dinghies. Though they penetrated the harbour area and spent hours wandering among the installations – with Fitzroy Maclean occasionally reprimanding Italian sentries for their evident lack of enthusiasm for their duties – both dinghies proved unusable through punctures suffered *en route*, and this party, too, left the area with no worthwhile triumphs to report.

But while Stirling's second Benghazi venture was in progress, Tramp Allott had been having an exciting time on the other side of the Cyrenaican bulge.

Eighth Army Headquarters, under the erroneous impression that they were about to drive Rommel back once more into Tripolitania ('The Bear blew first!'), required information regarding the possibilities of landing troops in diversionary attacks from the sea at various points along the coast, so Allott and Lieutenant Duncan Ritchie R.N. were landed with folboat, stores and radio set to investigate the beaches at Cape Ras el Tin.

By dawn they were holed up on a low sandhill fringed with stunted bushes some fifty yards from the shore, acutely aware of the fact that there was no other cover for miles around and that the delays incurred during the passage had put them several hours and a good mile and a half from their proposed dawn position. The morning produced nothing other than the boredom and thirst which are inevitable in such situations, but at noon a staff car drove up to disgorge three German officers, who indulged in a cooling bathe such as the two Britons were pining for. They did not seem at first to offer much of a threat to Allott and Ritchie, who watched them with no more inimical feeling than envy; but very shortly afterwards the sounds of martial singing were heard, and trucks arrived bearing some 200 German soldiers.

These, too, flung themselves eagerly into the sea and for the first hour or so offered no threat to the watchers. But after most of them had come ashore, dried off and lain about in the sun for a while, some of them out of boredom began playing – of all games – hide and seek. Fortunately not all took part, and fortunately the sandhill and its fringe of shrubs were too far away for the majority to take the trouble to reach; but a few did, and Allott and Ritchie were only saved from discovery by the scanty covering of sand they had flung over themselves, together with the fact that their bush was at the back of the clump and that sunbathing and the sea soon enticed the Germans back towards the main beach. But it was six o'clock before the now pink but tired *Soldaten* climbed back on their lorries and struck up the *Horst Wessel Lied* as they departed, by which time Allott and Ritchie were both parched and exhausted.

That night Allott sent off a signal – having, for the first time in S.B.S. history, taken a transmitter with him – briefly reporting on the tactical features of the beach; then, after a hurried meal, the two men launched out to sea again. That night the weather deteriorated sharply and Allott simplified his task by throwing the radio overboard, but the two spent the next three nights paddling along the hostile coast, occasionally having to drift silently and keep a very low profile as enemy shipping chugged by and in the intervening daylight hours surveying somewhat cursorily the beaches on which they had landed at dawn.

They were much relieved on the morning of May 26th to arrive in the Gazala inlet – somewhat to the surprise of the South African troops there – and even more relieved to be sent immediately to Tobruk and then on back to Alexandria. During the afternoon of the day they landed, Rommel's infantry closed up to the South Africans under cover of a blinding sandstorm, and that night the Afrika Korps panzers hooked around to the south of Bir Hacheim to initiate the long and arduous series of battles which ended with a tired and fragmented Eighth Army 400 miles back between Alamein and the Qattara Depression.

That really would have been a long paddle.

David Stirling, who was undoubtedly an expansionist at heart – he has been likened to a 'military Marks and Spencer' – had not allowed the failures at Buerat and Benghazi to affect his ambitions either to work much closer with the S.B.S. or to have his own seaborne section. In May, 1942, it became evident to Cairo H.Q. that the Axis forces were now in a position to mount such a blockade on Malta that the island was in danger of starvation unless supplies could get through to them, so it was suggested to Stirling that his organisation should mount a series of raids against Axis airfields during June in order to distract Luftwaffe attention from an attempted fast convoy from Alexandria to the embattled island.

The targets in Benghazi, Derna and Barce were enough to absorb practically all of Stirling's available trained strength, but there were airfields on Crete which would also need attention, and Mike Kealy agreed that S.B.S. teams would attack these. He reckoned, however, without Stirling's political ingenuity and in due course found that while his teams would go in and attack the airfields at Kastelli, Tymbaki and Maleme, the really succulent target at Heraklion would be attacked by a team consisting of a Greek guide, four Frenchmen from Stirling's latest manpower acquisitions under command of a Commandant Bergé, escorted and advised by Captain Lord Jellicoe, upon whom had descended the task of commanding any S.A.S. seaborne element.

Neither Kealy nor the other S.B.S. officers were very pleased about this allocation but, as one of them later wrote, opposing Stirling was like trying to stop a steam-roller with a banana. However reluctantly, they acquiesced and began preparations.

The various parties left Alexandria on June 6th, and four days later the S.B.S. contingents were on the way to their individual targets, having been met by one of the more famous of the M.O.4 representatives, Captain Tom Dunbabin, who

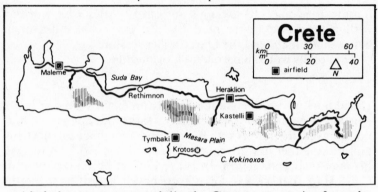

resided almost permanently in the Cretan mountains from the time of the German invasion in 1941 until its liberation at the end of 1944. After being briefed on the routes to their targets and how best to deal with the Cretan peasants who would undoubtedly identify them immediately as British and flock to their aid, the parties left and well on time were in position observing their targets. David Sutherland at Tymbaki was aggrieved to discover that the airfield had been abandoned and that there were no aircraft for him to destroy, while Mike Kealy and Tramp Allott were equally disappointed to find themselves forced to the conclusion that Maleme airfield was too well guarded to give them the slightest chance of success. The Germans had lost many thousands of their crack paratroops in the fight for Maleme and had no intentions of surrendering it or allowing infiltration. It was completely surrounded by wire fences at least one of which was electrified, machine-gun posts and searchlights had been installed at tactically well-chosen points all around it, and 'there were so many police dogs about that the place sounded like Crufts on show-day.'

George Duncan, however, accompanied by Sergeant Barnes and Corporal Barr, was much more fortunate at Kastelli. The quarry was lined up on the airstrip and the defences were derisory; within two hours they had placed bombs on eight aircraft, six trucks, four bomb dumps, seven petrol and two oil dumps. Every time delay and charge worked perfectly, and Duncan and his men were already some distance away when the whole area of the field began to erupt, aircraft and trucks

disintegrated, flames from the petrol and oil dumps shot into
the air, and with thunderous explosions the bomb dumps blew
up, killing, they later learned, at least seventy enemy soldiers.
To add an extra, sinister, score, reports later reached Cairo
that when the German authorities had satisfied themselves as
to the approach and departure routes taken by the party, they
ordered all sentries on duty there at the time to be shot for
carelessness.

Jellicoe and the Frenchmen, however, had not had an easy
ride at any stage.

Their four-day journey from Alexandria to the seas off
Heraklion had been marred by various unfortunate factors.
The operation had been hurriedly prepared and the four
Frenchmen and Greek guide, Lieutenant Costi, had had little
opportunity to get to know either each other or Jellicoe, and no
opportunity at all to adapt to submarine life. The excellent
rations aboard had been supplemented by a large stock of fresh
melons, and the French habit of dropping the half-eaten
remains on to the deck and then leaving them there aroused
strong feelings among the submarine crew, not subsequently
soothed by the French attitude that anything said to them in
any other language than their own hardly merited their
attention.

There was thus a feeling of noticeable relief aboard H.M.
Submarine *Triton* when, at about 2200 on June 10th,
the raiding party of six men clambered down into two
inflatable rubber boats (of German manufacture), which
Triton then proceeded to tow closer inshore. The conditions
were ideal: no wind and a flat calm – but when they were still
some two miles from the shore, an R.A.F. raid on the party's
objective caused a spectacular display of searchlight beams
against which *Triton* could easily have been silhouetted. After
a brief consultation the tows were slipped, and the raiders
departed on what proved to be a two-and-a-half-hour paddle,
unduly prolonged by the leaky condition of the boats. Jellicoe,
never very particular about his appearance, obligingly
sacrificed his best service dress cap as a bailer.

At last ashore, they faced the problem of disposing of the
boats in a way that would neither betray their presence nor
compromise the beaches for further operations, so while the

Frenchmen repacked rucksacks and prepared themselves for an arduous march, Jellicoe swam out to sea for some 200 yards, towing behind him the boats loaded with pebbles. He then sank them by pressing out the remaining air from the floatation bags, but it was a wearing and time-consuming task, and with the other delays suffered, it meant that when the party eventually left the beach they were already three hours behind schedule.

The march itself proved to be far more difficult than had been foreseen. Although they crossed the coast road easily enough (the patrolling sentries were almost all smoking), the ridges they then faced proved far more precipitous than reconnaissance or aerial photographs had revealed, and the task of climbing the almost vertical rocks while heavily burdened with weapons, maps, general equipment and rucksacks, each containing at least twelve bombs and weighing over 50lbs., was perturbing to say the least. Particularly unsettling was the thought that if one of the party fell and landed badly, a crushed detonator would blow rucksack and wearer to smithereens as well as drawing unwanted attention upon the whole party.

Just before dawn, with some relief, they found a cave and chose to lie up there for the day, but despite the exhausted sleep into which four members of the party promptly fell, both Jellicoe and Bergé were kept awake not only by the benzedrine tablets they had taken during the march, but also by the burdens of command, exacerbated by the fact that the occasional Cretan peasant they had encountered in the early morning had greeted them in enthusiastic but fractured English, while others who had passed during the day had all waved cheerfully at them. During the rest of their approach march, whenever they encountered Cretans they demanded in German to see their papers, adopting as they did so a somewhat hectoring attitude; but few of the Cretans were deceived, most departing on their way with much head-shaking and chuckling. It was difficult for Bergé and Jellicoe to decide whether to be worried by the lack of security or reassured by the obvious friendliness of the natives.

Despite all these complications, however, plus the necessity to make a half-circle approach march, the party were in position to observe the airfield by the evening of the

13th, and Commandant Bergé counted over sixty aircraft on the field, mostly Ju.88s. Unfortunately it proved impossible to attack that night, as unexpected sentry posts along a ridge delayed them, so they spent the next day completing their detailed plans, lying up in a vineyard 'growing thirsty on sour grapes' and occasionally chatting with an old Cretan labourer who was quite unconcerned by their presence and, in the evening, with a younger one who fetched them water.

Then, leaving Costi and the heavier stores in a cave, Jellicoe and the Frenchmen moved off while it was still light to within half a mile of the first defences, made conscious now that they were late in their attack by flights of Ju.88s taking off – obviously to attack the convoy Jellicoe and his men were endeavouring to protect – and returning shortly afterwards, some of them doing the German equivalent of a Victory Roll, which 'greatly exasperated' them.

At 2230, at last, Bergé gave the signal and they all moved forward into the attack, close alongside a barrack hut towards a belt of Dannert Wire. As they reached it, a German patrol came down the far side, its leader flashing a torch but apparently not sufficiently alert to notice Jellicoe's large and curly head protruding from the far-side ditch. His immediate follower, however, was not so inattentive and immediately enquired loudly and with some menace what was going on, his comrades gathering around to add force to his enquiry. They 'questioned us as to whom we were and we were unable immediately to produce a satisfactory answer.'

In this impasse, however, Corporal Mouhot became inspired. He produced a ghastly, lingering, drunken snore which so upset the German patrol that they moved off along the wire, muttering with some distaste among themselves, leaving Jellicoe and his party rapidly to cut their way through the wire and hastily conceal themselves in a bomb dump a mere twenty yards away. They were wise to move so quickly, because very shortly afterwards the patrol leader had second thoughts, turned his men around for further investigation, and, quickly discovering the newly-cut hole in the fence, called up another patrol and held a council of war.

Matters might then have become very difficult for the raiders but fortunately a diversion occurred. A flight of Ju.88s. returned at that moment, closely followed by a pair of R.A.F.

Blenheims who made the correct landing signals until they were over the field, then dropped their bombs and zoomed away. In the confusion that followed, the raiders moved out on to the main field and took cover in a fold in the ground from which they watched and waited until the airfield was quiet again. They then moved off, first of all into the blast-proof shelters in which aircraft were housed, where they placed charges on the wings and tailplanes of sixteen Ju.88s., avoiding patrolling sentries quite easily and leaving undisturbed the personnel actually sleeping in the shelters.

Their next move was across to the other side of the field, delayed occasionally by searchlight beams illuminating the runways as more flights of aircraft came in to land. They planted charges on another plane about to take off and also upon a light Feiseler-Storch reconnaissance plane, more upon crated aircraft engines, and then found, with some frustration, that one promising-looking group of dispersed aircraft to which they had moved with great care and patience, was composed of parked derelicts.

They were now recalled somewhat abruptly to the realities of the situation by the explosion of some of their first charges and the realisation that dawn was now only an hour and a half away. It was time they got out – a move which they accomplished with unexpected ease by 'mingling with the slightly harassed occupants' thronging the main barrack complex and then walking out through the main exit behind a dozen or so German ground staff, placing their remaining charges on a number of trucks as they did so.

By 0800 they were back at the dump, where they were delighted to find that Lieutenant Costi had procured an excellent meal of bread, soup, roast chicken and local wine from the nearest village. This they enjoyed enormously and then lay down for a well-deserved sleep – though again, too much benzedrine prevented Bergé and Jellicoe from taking full advantage of the break.

Now they were faced with the prospect of crossing the width of Crete, including two ranges of hills and the Plain of Mesara, in time to make the rendezvous – a task made more difficult by the fact that they were already a day late in the schedule and also by an error made on their first night's trek which took them in a half-circle and landed them at dawn no further away from Heraklion than they had been when they started out. Fortunately, they then met an old acquaintance of Lieutenant Costi's, who fed them and provided them with a guide for the next stage of the journey – to the village of Karkadhiotissa, where they rested for two days, sleeping in the open under rugs provided by the locals, from which, unfortunately, they all became afflicted with lice. Here they also learned of a rumour that sixty Cretan hostages had been shot as a reprisal for their raid, but were relieved to see that although this depressed their local friends, it did not seem to affect their generosity or friendliness.

On the 17th they walked on southwards, lying up the following day in a river bed, which, although it provided no food, allowed them to wash themselves and their clothes to some effect. Well rested, they crossed the plain that night and then made a detour which allowed Lieutenant Costi to visit his family, accompanied by Commandant Bergé. They returned sad but resolute: Costi's brothers had already left their home and were living as 'brigands' in the hills; his sisters were afraid to sleep at home, and his parents told of ever-increasing oppression from the Germans, reaching out now even towards the smallest Cretan villages. Nevertheless, his mother had given him two chickens for his friends.

The rest of the story is best told in Jellicoe's own words:

> As always, it was found impossible the next day to avoid contact with the peasants who all appeared friendly. One in particular, brought us some excellent wine and we questioned Lieutenant Costi about him, who said he was not only a personal acquaintance of his but an excellent man. That afternoon Commandant Bergé and the French party rested in a small valley on the Northern slopes of the hills to the south of the Plain. I went forward with Lieutenant Costi as guide, to get into contact with our agents in Krotos, whom I met that evening. Leaving Lieutenant Costi at Krotos, as he was tired, I went back with one of the agents to bring the main party to the rendezvous with the Special Boat Section. It was then dark, and although I searched the ground carefully where the party had been, I was unable to discover them. The agent was unwilling to stay there in daylight, so I sent him back to Krotos and searched further for evidence as to where the party was. Some young local peasants from the neighbouring village arrived in a great state of agitation, and from what was said and the signs used, I was led to understand that

Commandant Bergé had been betrayed and attacked by a party of Germans. After a resistance in which one of his party was killed, he had surrendered and been led off. I had had suspicions that something had gone wrong owing to finding traces of a meal tidily arranged. From my knowledge of the French, I knew, firstly, that nothing would have been left over and secondly, if it had, it would not have been tidily arranged.

They told me that the German patrol was returning to the area and advised me to flee. This I did and contacted the agent in Krotos whom I was lucky enough to run into on the track. When I told him what had happened, he became incoherent with fear and I was forced to abandon all co-operation with him. I was wearing civilian clothes at the time and was unarmed. By pure chance that evening I met Lieutenant Costi with a local peasant with whom he had spent the night. This man, Miroyannis, was fully aware of the situation and of the risks he was running in sheltering Lieutenant Costi. He immediately welcomed and fed me and showed me where the main rendezvous with the Special Boat Section was, whom I contacted that evening. Miroyannis himself went back to the area where Commandant Bergé had been captured to find out news of him. He confirmed the impressions I had received from the peasant and stated that the German patrols were searching for Lieutenant Costi and myself and said that Commandant Bergé and the remaining prisoners had been transferred to Heraklion. It was clearly impossible to do anything to help them.[4]

Three days later, both survivors were taken off one of the southern beaches in a small boat which also collected David Sutherland and his group, plus one each of Lieutenant Costi's brothers and sisters and another twenty miscellaneous refugees – 'mostly brigands, called patriots in this part of the world.'

The four raids had between them accounted for twenty-six aircraft, fifteen to twenty trucks, unknown but sizeable quantities of petrol, oil and bombs, and caused the deaths of over 100 enemy soldiers – at a cost of one Frenchman killed and three others taken prisoner. Another casualty was apparently the *amour propre* of the hall porter of the Cecil Hotel at Alexandria, who was somewhat surprised at Jellicoe's appearance as he swept by on the way towards a much-needed drink, 'as I was very curiously dressed.'

There now occurred a series of events which was to change irrevocably both the nature of the S.B.S. teams and the nature of the targets which they would attack.

In view of the dangers inherent in operations so far the Special Boat Sections had suffered remarkably few casualties, but no formation engaged upon such hazardous work during the years 1940 to 1945 could expect to continue functioning without at some time or another experiencing a period of disaster. One such occurred to the inheritors of Roger Courtney's tradition in the Mediterranean during the third quarter of 1942, beginning in July when a party including both George Duncan and Eric Newby were landed in Sicily and all almost immediately captured. This was followed in August when another party was briefed to land at Daba, quite close behind the German defences opposite Alamein, in order to attack the landing-strip there.

The approach to the target was through a camp area in which tents were pitched in neat lines, and a cinema and canteen were still doing business despite the lateness of the hour – business for front-line soldiers, moreover, who were well aware of the enemy's raiding proclivities and thus by nature and training far more alert than second-line troops guarding supply lines miles from any apparent danger. The results were probably inevitable: many pairs of S.B.S. men failed to reach their targets altogether and left their charges on anything which struck them as vulnerable, and of the two pairs who did reach the strip, one pair were forced to retire after attacking only a bomb dump and some captured British transport, while the other pair were seen and efficiently fired upon. Corporal Gurney was wounded so badly that he could not move, and Mike Alexander remained with him, both men – highly talented operators – being taken prisoner.

Then during September occurred one of the most spectacularly successful but expensive operations carried out during this first, almost legendary, phase of S.B.S. history.

During May and June a party containing Tommy Langton, Eric Newby and David Sutherland had spent a very pleasant six weeks engaged upon the reconnaissance of some thirty beaches along the Syrian shore. At this time, Rommel was driving eastwards towards the Nile, while Kleist's Army Group South threatened the Caucasus, and if both broke through it seemed probable to strategists in Whitehall and Cairo that they might aim for a link-up at the head of the Persian Gulf – towards which Kleist's forces must pass through Syria; in which case, Special Service troops left behind might fight as guerillas, and knowledge of beaches across which they might be reinforced and supplied would be of value.

Though the positions at Alamein and Stalingrad were to hold and the threat never become real, the work carried out by Sutherland and his companions gave them experience of both operational survey and reconnaissance, and also, it would seem, a taste for the eastern littoral of the Mediterranean. Towards the end of August, Sutherland returned there, accompanied this time by Tramp Allott, Sergeant Moss, Corporal McKenzie, Private Blake and Marines Duggan, Barrow and Harris. They made their headquarters in the then delightful town of Beirut, and were joined in due course by Captain Tsoucas of the Royal Hellenic Army, by Sub-Lieutenant Calambakidis of the Royal Hellenic Navy and by two other Greeks, Nicolas Savvas and Georgeos Kyrmihali, who had volunteered to act as guides. The objectives for this collection of what has been called 'licensed brigands' were situated on the very island which had been the original planned objective for Layforce when they left England – Rhodes.

The Luftwaffe and the Regia Aeronautica were using two operational airfields on Rhodes from which to harass Allied shipping in the eastern Mediterranean, and also to exercise almost complete control over the seaways up and into the Aegean. These airfields were near Marizza in the north of the island, and at Calato, halfway down the eastern coastline – and it was the intention of Allott and Sutherland to divide their forces into two parties and wreak as much damage on the two airfields as they could during the night of 12th/13th September; with which intention they took their men aboard His Hellenic Majesty's Submarine *Papanikolis* and sailed from Beirut during the afternoon of 31st August.

The four days of the voyage were passed in conditions of cramped boredom exacerbated as usual by language

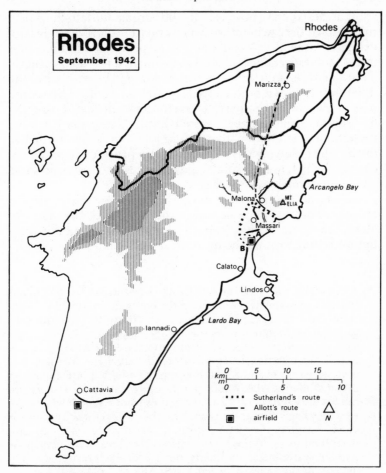

Rhodes
September 1942

Rhodes

Marizza

Arcangelo Bay

Malona
MT ELIA
Massari
A
B

Calato

Lindos

Iannadi
Lardo Bay

Cattavia

```
 0        5        10       15
km|_____|_____|_____|
m|_____|_____|
 0               5               10
••••  Sutherland's route
————  Allott's route
 ■    airfield                    N
```

difficulties, though on this occasion no ill-feeling developed as everyone's attitude was obviously friendly. On the night of September 4th/5th, after a periscope reconnaissance of the landing beach, the party left the submarine in perfect conditions aboard three rubber dinghies and a fol-boat, and although a slight set in the tide took them marginally off course, the beach on which they made their landings, after a two-hour paddle, proved ideal for concealment of all the equipment they wished to leave there.

A major problem always faced by parties landing from

submarines is that however fit and strong those taking part might have been when they went aboard, a few days' lack of exercise in the airless confines of a torpedo flat will take their toll – a toll especially evident during the first few hours ashore. That factor combined – as on Crete in June – with the difference between physical reality and the contour lines on a map, now slowed the party to such an extent that during the first night's march they covered hardly more than a mile, though fortunately they then found a cave in which to shelter during the following day. This cave also provided them with a cache in which to hide spare equipment, Mae Wests and some signalling torches against their return.

David Sutherland's account of the next two days illustrates an apparently ineluctable law – that approach marches are always more tiring than one expects and beset by difficulties unforeseeable by even the most prescient – not to say cynical – planner.

From this moment onwards the going was extremely difficult, and together with the heavy load and the doubt of the guides as to the right route to take, the progress of the party was exceptionally slow. Due to frequent halts the distance covered by 0400 hrs. was little over a mile, then Capt. Allott and myself decided that it was out of the question to cross the road that night. We therefore searched for a hideout, and eventually found a grotto capable of accommodating the whole party. Once established there the guides were sent to fill 12 water bottles from a source which they said they knew of near the road. They however returned just before dawn without water reporting enemy activity in the neighbourhood of their destination. The next day was spent without water but in the shade; during the day I observed enemy activity in the valley between MASSARI and CALATO, on the aerodrome itself, and noted various positions and defence systems.

Night 6/7. Before dusk the guides were sent to recce the route for the night's march, as it was imperative to reach the road if water was to be obtained. They still insisted on keeping to the side of Mt. ELIA in lieu of the valley, which they believed to be patrolled after dark. A similar march to that of the night before resulted, and again the party made its final halt about one mile from the MALONA bridge. Owing to the nature of the ground and load, the Greek interpreters showed distinct signs of exhaustion due to lack of training in such marching, and slowed the party down by frequent halts. Determined to get water that night, I sent the guides together with Mnes. Barrow and Harris into the valley with instructions not to return without 14 water bottles filled. They returned just after first light, and the party laid up on the hillside directly opposite MASSARI.

Two valuable nights had thus been wasted by taking the mountain route. The guides at first said they knew the way, and latterly openly confessed that they were ignorant of their surroundings. One can hardly blame them as they had volunteered to come on the operation at great risk to themselves. It is however advisable to ascertain how much a guide really knows about the country before entrusting him to lead a party. No guide is better than a bad one.

Captain Allott and myself decided that for the sake of speed on his journey to MARITZA [*sic*], the parties should separate on the night 7/8. This meant that he had 5 nights in which to reach his objective, operate on the night 12/13, and still have five nights clear to make his way back to the beach. I also advocated lightening the load by carrying minimum food, and dumping all excess weight where we were lying up, to which he agreed.[5]

Just after dark on the 7th, therefore, Tramp Allott, Sergeant Moss, Corporal McKenzie, Private Blake and Georgeos Kyrmihali moved off on their long trek up to Marizza, and half an hour later Sutherland took his party down into the valley, across the road bridge at Malona and began the semi-circular approach to the north-west angle of the Calato field. He had with him the Greek Sub-Lieutenant Calambakidis, Marines Duggan, Barrow and Harris, and the guide Nicolas Savvas. They had five nights in which to complete a comparatively short journey.

By the same token, of course, they also had five days and nights of extreme discomfort, for the weather was bitterly cold, and five days and nights also in which to be discovered and betrayed – though as it happened only two shepherds were encountered on the way and these proved friendly and co-operative, bringing them food and water and providing quite a lot of useful information regarding enemy defences and patrolling habits. The daylight hours of the 12th were spent by Sutherland observing his target from an excellent vantage point and making the plans upon which he briefed the rest of the party that evening.

The aircraft which constituted the main target were grouped in two areas. In the larger group on the north-east side of the area were three Savioa-Macchetti 84s, five Macchi 202s. and six Capronis, all close together and with an uncounted number of extra aircraft sheltered in some olive trees a little way off to the north-west. The smaller group consisted of some seventeen Savioa-Macchetti 84s. actually inside the aerodrome itself, well dispersed and probably better guarded than the ones outside the barrack area.

Obviously the first group constituted the more worthwhile target and the one upon which best results would probably be obtained; they thus merited the strongest concentration of force. The group inside the drome itself would be less vulnerable, but an attack upon it might act as a means of distraction from the main business being carried out to the north-east, although such a ploy would undoubtedly increase the danger in which those carrying it out would operate. But it seemed to Sutherland to be worth the risk.

Bombs were made up and distributed – twenty-two to A Party, fifteen to B Party; rucksacks were dumped, spare water-bottles and kit sent back to the arranged R.V. with Savvas, the guide. Parties would withdraw separately to this R.V., wait there for the other party until 0400, then start off into the hills to find a hiding-place for the day. Sub-Lieutenant Calambakidis and Sutherland made quite certain that they both knew the area in which the other party would be operating in order to avoid unfortunate coincidences, and also that every man in both parties knew the projected routes in and out of the target areas and the exact timings for the operation. They moved off together at 2015, reached and crossed the road at 2255 and separated in the dry bed of a river at 2315. The night was very dark and it was raining heavily; Sutherland and Marine Duggan moved off towards the aerodrome defences, Calambakidis with Marines Barrow and Harris disappeared down towards the main targets.

Sutherland and Duggan approached the north-west corner of the aerodrome and came across their first prey, unexpectedly, outside the wire: three Savioa-Macchetti 84s. parked together and guarded by a single sentry who obligingly moved off at midnight. Within minutes all three were garlanded with bombs and then both men dropped into a ditch alongside the outer wire, through which, a few moments afterwards, they cut their way. As the only route to their main group of targets was along a passageway between two huts, they walked along it, with outward confidence but some trepidation – quickly to realise that their trepidation had been well founded. Halfway down, a sentry stepped out from the shadows and challenged them, and when they retreated somewhat precipitately he followed, shouting towards a lighted hut which promptly disgorged several of his compatriots who began diligently to search the area.

Fortunately the Italians concentrated their efforts inside the wire, unaware that Sutherland and Duggan had not paused until they found themselves back in the ditch from which they had first entered the camp, from which they now observed subsequent events. Cool thought revealed that despite the indignity of their present position and the obvious impossibility of now attacking targets inside the aerodrome, they were still performing their vital function: they had attracted all hostile attention towards their side of the target area, leaving the far side and the main objective unattended except by A Party, who were presumably distributing their explosives among the parked Savioas, Macchis and Capronis there, unhindered by enemy attention.

At 0100 Sutherland decided that it was time he and Duggan left for the first rendezvous, but they still had several bombs between them to put to good use, so some they placed upon and around a petrol dump and the rest they placed on the three bombers they had already decorated, thus ensuring their complete destruction. They left the area just before 0200 and had covered less than a quarter of a mile when the first of their charges went off, followed shortly after by the ones on the other two aircraft and the petrol dump. Then at 0230 explosions began on the far side of the airfield where A Party had been busy, and from then on a continuous rumble as of gunfire followed them back to the R.V., which they reached at 0330. As their meeting-place was located at the first high point on their escape route, they could for the first time gain some idea of the results they and their companions had achieved.

Fifteen fires blazed around the sides of the aerodrome, some of them so large that they obviously consisted of more than one plane; indeed, in A Party's area the Savioas and Macchis had been parked so close together that they might well have set each other ablaze. Bomb dumps, petrol and oil dumps exploded, ammunition crackled continuously and a fiery red glow suffused the underside of the clouds above the whole valley area – lit now also by searchlight beams playing over the valley floor and the lower reaches of the hills. Evidently there was no doubt in the enemy's mind how the attack had been mounted and how its perpetrators intended to escape.

Then, just before 0400, bursts of machine-gun fire were heard from the foothills just north of the aerodrome, followed by a burst from a Tommy-gun, and a series of flashing lights converging on one spot. A Party were obviously in trouble, though to what extent only time would tell; but as, ominously, there was no sign of them by 0430, Sutherland reluctantly decided he must abide by his own orders, and he, Marine Duggan and the guide Savvas set off.

> We had left little time in which to be concealed before dawn, and were hampered by the attentions of a searchlight flashing on us from the beach east of the aerodrome. The guide refused to go on whilst in the vicinity of the beam, and stopped so frequently that he eventually had to be left behind, Mne. Duggan and myself proceeded alone into some rough ground. The guide being quite capable of hiding himself I was not anxious as regards his safety.[6]

The two men lay up during the 13th at a spot from which they could watch events on the airfield to some extent, although rain and low cloud still limited visibility. Burnt-out planes littered the area, ground staff scurried to and fro, and at about 0930 a large plane landed, to be immediately surrounded by personnel running in from every angle, obviously to report. It looked as though a senior official had arrived to count up the losses – and perhaps to collect prisoners, if Sutherland's fears for A Party were justified. That night he and Duggan climbed on upwards to reach Captain Tsoucas's hideout, and the three discussed future possibilities.

There was no doubt that the raid on Calato had been a success and that the Italian and German commands would be extremely angry; they were by now sufficiently aware of the activities of British raiding parties to guess the next moves, so now patrols would be sent along the nearby coasts in order to prevent re-embarkation. Speed would be of the essence; the raiders must therefore reach the rendezvous with Allott's party as quickly as possible, make contact with the submarine and get off the island.

The three set off the next night. The journey to the landing beach was complicated by the need to find water and at one point by the discovery of what looked like extensive minefields across their route, but by the 15th they were lying up in the foothills of Mount Elia awaiting Allott and his men. During the morning all seemed well, but then in mid-afternoon they suddenly saw a group of about twenty-four soldiers accompanied by six civilians approaching from across a valley, splitting into two and beginning what was quite obviously an encircling movement.

Quickly the three gathered their kit and, despite protests from Captain Tsoucas that he was too old and unfit for such activity, they climbed first to a small cave and then, as this would be too obvious a hiding-place, further on up the hillside to a small, sloping ledge with a protective wall behind. As they flung themselves down panting, more small parties came around the other side of the mountain and began searching the slopes below, each party containing a civilian obviously acting as guide. Only Sutherland's insistence on the second step of the climb had saved them – and that only by a few minutes – but for the next two hours they lay there, unprotected except by the lack of realisation by the searchers as to how far and how fast men can climb when their liberty is at stake.

One party did come within ten yards of their ledge, but their attention was then caught – and that of the men above them riveted – by events down by the beach. An Italian M.T.B. had appeared from the direction of Lindos, and, after cruising slowly along the beachline, suddenly turned in and disappeared from the watchers' sight, ominously close to their landing beach. Twenty minutes later she appeared again, towing behind her three black objects only too recognisable as their Carley Floats, while a black smudge on the deck seemed all too likely to be the folboat. After that the search parties continued to move about in a somewhat half-hearted manner until dusk, when they congregated and then moved off, leaving Sutherland, Tsoucas and Duggan facing a situation which could only be called critical.

They were without food, and their means of re-embarkation

was gone. Moreover, Allott's party and those of Sub-
Lieutenant Calambakidis's who were still at liberty (and it
might be all of them) were due to arrive at the beach below
during the next twenty-four hours – and were presumably
unaware either of recent events or that the beach was
compromised. And equally unaware would be the captain of
the submarine due to pick them all up on the night of the
17th/18th.

During the following night and day (ten hours
spent lying in the sun without food or water!) Sutherland
pondered the position and made his plans; and at 2000 on the
16th all three men crept down to a shepherd's hut at the foot
of the mountain and filled both their stomachs and their
water-bottles from the trough there, after which Tsoucas
returned to the ledge with everything but Sutherland's and
Duggan's small-arms. The other two, with infinite caution,
then located and finally entered the small cave in which they
had left the signalling torches and Mae Wests, finding to their
relief that these had been undisturbed; they collected their
own and moved off again at 2330, leaving a message tied to
one of the remaining torches reading, '*Boats captured, signalling
and swimming from intended landing beach.*'

They had hardly set out when there was suddenly a great
commotion in the area of the ledge to which Tsoucas had
presumably retired. Torches were flashed and there was much
shouting, so the two men spent the next hour in painstaking
reconnaissance and stalking which established that there was
now a considerable body of enemy troops between them and
Tsoucas – *if* he was still at liberty; more particularly, that
same force lay between the beach and the direction from
which Allott's party were expected. Evidently, one of the
guides had been caught and induced by some means or
another to talk.

Dawn revealed thirty or forty Italian soldiers congregated
about 400 yards away from where Sutherland and Duggan
were hiding, and within a few more minutes they were joined
by others. It was obvious that a thorough search of the area
was intended. The two crept under a huge rock and prepared
themselves for the worst – but in fact the worst that happened
to them was that for five or ten minutes one of the Italian
soldiers actually sat on the rock under which they were hiding,

while all the time the sun beat down and the space in which they were lying immobile became hotter and more cramped.

Then at 1330 there was another sudden diversion. A message arrived on the beach, the bulk of the soldiers were formed up with full equipment and two machine-guns and marched away, and half an hour later the sound of firing came from the cave from which they had collected their torches and Mae Wests, followed by much shouting and more commotion. Somebody had been caught (it was in fact Calambakidis and A Party from Calato), and although unfortunate for them, the episode provided relief for Sutherland and Duggan. The enemy soldiers moved away, the rest of the day was quiet and, as the sun at last declined, cooler. Now it remained to see who else, if anyone, would arrive for the pick-up, if enemy night patrols along the beach could be avoided, and if contact could be made with the submarine.

Night 17/18. Moved off at 2000 hrs, rested and watered at the trough, arrived at beach where we proposed to land originally 2040 hours. No sign of enemy patrols; Captain Tsoucas did not appear, so I sent Mne. Duggan to search towards C. ARCANGELO in case he had missed the position. He returned at 2115 hrs having seen no one. I therefore thought that he would see our signals and join up later. First 3 groups of Ks sent out at 2130 hrs. Mne Duggan thought he saw recognition directly seawards, but could not be certain (it was in fact flashed through the periscope as S/M was still submerged). I waited until 2200 hrs. and received the recognition from the S/M, replied Y and followed with the words "Swimming come in". The S/M was not visible through the binoculars when we entered the water directly afterwards. We swam for about an hour in the direction of the recognition until we heard the sound of engines, this I believed to be the S/M as I had previously been informed by Capt Allott that the ship's engines would be running to enable the party to locate her more easily. Mne Duggan gave occasional flashes with the torch, but the sound grew fainter and eventually disappeared. I later found out from the Captain HMS TRAVELLER that these were the engines of the Italian M.T.B. which attacked us just after I got on board. We were rather dispondent [*sic*] at hearing what we thought was the S/M apparently going away, but encouraged each other to continue. In spite of the calm sea, our physical condition for such a swim was hardly adequate owing to the recent strain added to the fact that we had only had one tin of

sardines each during 5 days, and little water. We were however
determined to reach the S/M in spite of the growing cold, and
much to our relief sighted her slightly to our right at about 2320
hrs. We were helped onto the fore planes, and inboard at 2330.[7]

H.M. Submarine *Traveller* promptly dived and was equally
promptly depth-charged by the boat whose engines had so
nearly enticed Sutherland and Duggan towards a tragic loss of
liberty, but no damage was done and within days she had
delivered them back to Beirut, where it was found that
Sutherland, a slight figure when he had set out on the
operation, had lost a stone, and that both men were ill with
strain and exhaustion.

Allott and all his party, Calambakidis and his, and Captain
Tsoucas had all been taken prisoner, and although Captain
Tsoucas made a classic series of escapes and was finally
successful in the summer of 1944, the others were to spend the
rest of the war in various prison camps. But Allott's raid on
Marizza had been as productive as Sutherland's on Calato, and
both Luftwaffe and Regia Aeronautica had been considerably
weakened.

Perhaps most important of all, from this operation
Sutherland learned many lessons which were to be put to good
use.

TWO

Reorganisation

SEPTEMBER '42 – JULY '43

With Roger Courtney and Mike Kealy back in England, Eric Newby, George Duncan, Tramp Allott and Tug Wilson prisoners (Wilson had been caught paddling 'with malice aforethought' around Tobruk Harbour in July shortly after the port had fallen), David Sutherland in hospital – to say nothing of the loss of such S.B.S. stalwarts as Sergeant Dunbar, Corporal Booth, Guardsman Duffy and Marines Barrow and Harris – yet another 'old original' was to disappear from the scene, though fortunately, only temporarily.

During the early summer of 1942, one of the legendary characters of the Desert War, Lieutenant-Colonel John Haselden (he had acted as guide for Geoffrey Keyes's raid on Beda Littoria) had spent a great deal of time behind Axis lines disguised as an Arab, collecting and sending back much valuable information. He had come back to Cairo at the end of July and in early August had suggested that he return to Tobruk with a few picked saboteurs and there blow up the bulk fuel storage tanks, which were so heavily concreted in as to be virtually immune from air attack, and that his party should then escape south into the desert to a rendezvous with the Long Range Desert Group.

In the circumstances of August, 1942, any suggestions for the destruction of more of Rommel's petrol supplies were welcomed with enthusiasm – but perhaps on this occasion with a little too much. Before many days had elapsed, a slightly bemused John Haselden found himself commanding a much larger force than he had ever contemplated, taking part in a combined operation of ever-increasing complexity.

The final plan for *Operation Daffodil*, as this attack on Tobruk was called, envisaged the penetration of the Tobruk defences along the El Adem-Tobruk road by a party of commandos with sappers and signallers attached, travelling in three lorries with Afrika Korps markings, the men disguised as prisoners-of-war with members of the highly secret Special Interrogation Group (S.I.G.) dressed in German uniforms acting the parts of lorry drivers and guards.

Having entered Tobruk, this force would seize the eastern-most inlet at Mersa Sciausc and capture the coastal guns in the neighbourhood, then hold the inlet while a company of Highlanders with machine-gunners attached came ashore from sixteen motor torpedo boats and three motor launches, which would all have made the journey along the coast from Alexandria. In the meantime on the other side of the harbour, a battalion of Royal Marines would have been landed from the destroyers H.M.Ss. *Sikh* and *Zulu*, and the two forces now ashore would fight their way into the port area, thus allowing both destroyers then to enter the harbour with yet more troops. All would then join in a positive orgy of destruction and sabotage which would render Tobruk useless as a supply port for the Panzerarmee now ranged up against the Alamein defences.

Neither was this to be the sole operation mounted that night. David Stirling was ordered to take a large party in forty heavily-armed jeeps into Benghazi; the Long Range Desert Group were to mount attacks on the airfields at Benina and Barce, while a detachment from the Sudan Defence Force took and held the oasis at Jalo through which the bulk of the raiding forces on all targets to the north would endeavour to escape.

John Haselden's original idea had therefore ballooned from a single operation carried out by a maximum of ten men, into four operations engaging a total strength of nearly 700 in the raids themselves and nearly as many in administration – not to speak of the naval contingent. This, in addition to the two destroyers, the M.T.Bs. and M.L.s. already listed, envisaged a protecting force against air and sea attack consisting of the cruiser H.M.S. *Coventry* and eight more Hunt class destroyers.

Wishful dreams and ambitions had far outrun practicality. Raiding forces did not then contain the numbers of trained and experienced operators needed to meet such large-scale demands, neither did the administration staffs, nor – most importantly of all – did the planning staffs. Stirling himself, his chief officers and most experienced men, the senior officers and men of the L.R.D.G. and, one suspects, John Haselden himself, were appalled not only by the size of the forces they were ordered to lead into actions for which most of them were unprepared, but also by the impracticality of many of the suggestions made by the enthusiastic planners at Cairo H.Q. Most of all, they were worried by the breaches in security that were obviously taking place even during the training period.

Their worst fears were realised only too well, for the series of operations mounted on the night of September 13th, 1942, led to almost complete disaster. Only at Barce, where thirty-two Axis aircraft and a dozen vehicles were destroyed, were any worthwhile results obtained; otherwise almost nothing was achieved, and the cost to the Allies was the cruiser *Coventry*, two destroyers, four M.T.Bs., two M.Ls., 280 naval officers and men, 300 Royal Marines and 160 soldiers – all lost on the Tobruk raid alone. The other raids were almost as costly in the valuable S.A.S. and L.R.D.G. men, but as it happened, only one S.B.S. man had been engaged, and he eventually got back.

Lieutenant Tommy Langton had been detailed to accompany the commando force into Tobruk and then to make himself responsible for reconnoitring the beaches each side of Mersa Sciausc inlet and for signalling in the M.T.Bs. and M.Ls. bringing the Highlanders and machine-gunners. It is typical of the confusion and inexperience which characterised the whole of this operation, that at the last moment he was saddled with additional responsibilities which effectively prevented him from carrying out any of his tasks properly. One of the detachment commanders developed dysentery on the way up, and Langton was appointed his second-in-command; thus, when the party debussed at the head of the inlet, Langton found that his first duty was to lead a section along the eastern side of the inlet – a journey complicated and seriously delayed by the discovery of a minefield through which sappers had first to find a way for them all, and then by a Spandau post which had to be attacked and silenced.

By this time a success signal had been fired by the party clearing the western side of the inlet, but although Langton had managed to reach and carry out a solitary examination of the beach on the eastern side, he could do nothing about the signalling, as the party detailed to clear the eastern headland (for which he had been ordered to assume some responsibility) was well behind schedule and, so far as he could judge, had lost their way and were veering too far eastwards.

Eventually the success signal for the eastern side was fired and Langton could race back towards the mouth of the inlet, where he was relieved to see that the officer whom he had persuaded to help him by signalling from the western headland was more or less in position (he was really too high up the cliffs), his red Aldis lamp flashing regularly and correctly. Unfortunately, Langton's duties as second-in-command of the eastern assault party had taken so long to carry out that he then had no time to return to the place where he had left his own Aldis lamp, and in this emergency, knowing that the M.T.Bs. and M.Ls. must now be offshore, desperately searching the blackness of the coast for the two sets of lights between which they must sail in, Langton endeavoured to help by signalling with his hand-torch. He synchronised his flashes with those from the other headland, but since his torch was obviously much weaker than an Aldis lamp – and white instead of red – and since the other Aldis was out of position, it was hardly surprising that only two of the M.T.Bs. made their way safely into the inlet, one of them almost immediately to become irretrievably stuck on a mud-bank.

But with even two of the M.T.Bs. in, it now became Langton's job to guide the soldiers on board up to Haselden's H.Q. so in some desperation he wedged his torch between two rocks and began the descent, only to see a third M.T.B. proceeding *away* from the inlet. He rushed back and recommenced signalling – unavailingly, as the M.T.B. muttered off into the blackness – but when he descended again to the spot where he had in his haste left his haversack and Tommy-gun, he found them both missing; and a few minutes later ran into two German soldiers carrying them. He opened fire with his revolver and frightened them away, reached the shore of the inlet to find the two M.T.Bs. discharging their cargoes of Highlanders and machine-gunners satisfactorily, so climbed back once again to the headland to resume his signalling – but as ineffectively as before.

By dawn it was quite evident that *Operation Daffodil* was a failure, though the extent of the disaster was not realised until much later. Those M.T.Bs. and M.Ls. not sunk or sinking were making their way back home along the coast; H.M.S. *Zulu,* with a badly-damaged H.M.S. *Sikh* in tow, was limping away from the port under shell-fire (soon to be replaced by concentrated air attack); and nearer to hand, the surviving commandos were being penned into an ever-decreasing circle by German and Italian troops, constantly reinforced as daylight increased and lorries poured in from the rest of the garrison area. An early attempt to break out of the circle was staged and led by John Haselden, but it was recognised for what it was even before it began moving and successfully ambushed, and Haselden himself was killed. As the local battle moved inexorably towards its conclusion, Langton and a few others boarded the beached M.T.B., put its Lewis guns to some use clearing the top of the western ridge and spent some time trying to get the engines started.

Failing in this ('I just don't know which bloody buttons to press!'), five of them boarded an assault craft and paddled out into the bay itself, pursued by machine-gun and rifle fire to such an effect that eventually they put into shore again. They then decided that their only means of escape from an obvious fiasco was to climb the cliffs up on to the main plateau and then make their way eastwards parallel to the coast, out through the eastern edge of the Tobruk perimeter and eventually, with luck, to Bardia, Egypt and their own lines.

It took Langton eight weeks, during which time his party had increased as a result of chance encounter and decreased as a result of illness. In that time he and the three who were still with him when they met British patrols near Himeimat – Corporal Wilson, Private Hillman (who was one of the S.I.G., a German Jew who would undoubtedly have been shot had he been captured) and Private Watler, who was to remain with Langton and join S.B.S. – had walked over 400 miles, much of it on their bare feet. They had been passed from Arab village to Arab village along the coast and stayed in the Wadi Qattara for nearly four weeks, being fed by the Arabs when possible and also collecting news. German and especially Italian morale was very low, they heard, and the Arabs had been astonished by the fact that an English raiding force had been able to reach Tobruk from Kuffra; the Arabs also seemed to have no doubt that the Allies would win the war, possibly reassured on this point by the fact that any fires lit during the night (this applied to Langton and his friends as well) invariably attracted a string of bombs from marauding aircraft.

Dysentery had so weakened three members of the original party that they had dropped out, and the last stage of the journey from Sollum down past Siwa to the southern border of the Qattara Depression, took the remaining four nineteen days – on three tins of bully beef, some goat-meat and Arab bread, and ten water-bottles. During this stage the only signs of life they saw were near Siwa when they spotted what could have been an S.A.S. patrol, but as it might have been the enemy, they avoided making contact.

This lack of activity was all the more surprising in view of the fact that during the first ten days of their walk into Egypt the Battle of Alamein was being fought, and from November 5th to the 9th they could have been caught up in the triumphant advance of the Eighth Army. Langton's irritation when he heard about this was understandable. 'If somebody had told me what was going on,' he remarked bitterly, 'I could have stayed where I was among the Arabs and just waited!'

The remark, however, was made during the course of a mess party held at the main S.A.S. base at Kabrit to celebrate Langton's return – for the independent life of the original 1st Special Boat Section had been terminated by the run of bad luck which had so decimated its ranks, allied to the turn-round in the fortunes of the Eighth Army once Montgomery and Alexander had assumed control of affairs in Egypt.

Neither general had had previous experience of using the sort of 'Private Army' that had sprung up in the desert scene, and after September 13th it would not have been surprising if all such enterprises had been abruptly discontinued. But even Montgomery was impressed by the reputation David Stirling and his men had won for themselves and was willing to accept that they had not been responsible for the *Daffodil* disasters, so for the moment they were allowed continued existence, as was the Long Range Desert Group. But those were the only two, and members of other unorthodox groups had either to return to their original formations – or join the S.A.S. Thus, Stirling's ambitions were realised, and such figures as Wally Hughes, Shaun O'Reilly, Laverick, Watson, Sergeant Henderson, Corporal Pomford, Sergeant Feeberry, Corporal Riley – and David Sutherland when he came out of hospital – found themselves alongside the Suez Canal, taking courses in parachute jumping (something, incidentally, that Sutherland had vowed he would never do even in his maddest moments) and thus qualifying to wear the beige beret and 'Winged Dagger' badge of the S.A.S., and also their special parachute emblem based on a symbolic Ibis with outstretched wings.

Whatever the others might have thought, Sutherland was delighted. For too long the S.B.S. had had to rely upon other organisations for a home, and upon an *ad hoc* system of administration which had left them at times dangerously exposed and short of vital equipment. More importantly, with the disappearance first of Roger Courtney and then of Mike Kealy there had been nobody to correlate operations, and thus no basic system to ensure that lessons learned on one raid were put to good use on the next. What was now needed was a firm base protected from bureaucratic interference by prestige in high places – and this David Stirling's organisation now provided – plus time in which to reorganise.

This last requirement, however, in turn produced a situation which did not please David Sutherland at all. Even when Sutherland had completed his parachute course, Stirling rigidly refused to allow him or any S.B.S. men to take part in the raids which he and his most experienced operators were carrying out well in advance of the Eighth Army as Montgomery drove inexorably westwards towards and across the Tunisian border. Instead, the S.B.S. were all to stay at the eastern end of the Mediterranean and be ready to undertake operations in the Aegean and perhaps the Adriatic, once the North African campaign was at an end and the war had moved over to the European shore.

In pursuit of this, Sutherland now commenced the training of fifty men, half of them English and half Greek from the newly attached Greek Sacred Squadron, placing the initial emphasis on the ability to march long distances over rough country, carrying increasingly heavy burdens. Associated abilities such as map-reading, use of captured weapons as well as those in the Allied armoury, use of explosives and the other techniques of sabotage, were all included in the training programme, as were folboat techniques, and – a new departure – the seamanship necessary to handle Greek caiques of all sizes in the unpredictable waters of the eastern Mediterranean, with some men trained to crew sailing schooners.

Lieutenant Kenneth Lamonby would assist Sutherland in the seamanship programme, and other officers would be appointed to help in other spheres of training as they became available. And as some consolation for the routine nature of his employment, Sutherland was allowed to take his fifty men up to his favourite stamping ground, the Lebanon, and base them in the Weygand Barracks in Beirut, where from his own room he could look down on the harbour and across St. Georges Bay as far as the red tongue of the Dog River.

As it happened, while Langton was still marching, Sutherland undergoing the heart-stopping excitements of the first parachute jumps and Stirling launching his raiding parties farther and farther ahead of the Eighth Army's advances, one of the last operations in the tradition of Tug Wilson and Wally Hughes was taking place.

The landing of Mark Clark and the other American officers had occurred on the evening of October 21st, and a few days later both Gruff Courtney and Jimmy Foot were on their way back to the U.K. But Dick Livingstone and his No.2., Sergeant Weatherall, remained in Gibraltar based on the submarine depot ship there, H.M.S. *Maidstone*, and on November 19th they took passage on H.M. Submarine *Ursula* for the Gulf of Genoa.

Conditions for the first stage of the voyage had hardly been propitious. For four days so violent a storm raged that its movement could be felt even at a depth of 120 feet, while at night, on the surface for the re-charging of the batteries, the sub pitched and rolled to such an extent that Livingstone became extremely ill and everything in the minuscule wardroom came adrift – even the table, which had been bolted down – every movable article smashing and crashing from side to side to the musical accompaniment of splintering crockery.

> Green seas swept the bridge, making watches a misery and also a danger: Lt. Oxborough was washed overboard and lost from the submarine in this storm. The unfortunate officer of the watch came below dripping and weary to find a pile of miscellaneous gear blocking the alley and filling the wardroom. The sea came down the conning-tower hatch and put the sounding machine out of action and damaged some of the electrical gear in the control-room. The gyro-compass jammed and one of the Diesels blew a gasket ... Sleep was impossible at night; one had to hold on to avoid being pitched across the ship, and I could only endure in misery until the welcome klaxon announced our descent at dawn to comparative peace.[1]

At one moment the captain of the submarine seriously considered turning back and abandoning the cruise, but fortunately the weather moderated and his engineers were able to repair most of the damage to enable them to carry on. Three nights later they were off Toulon when they were puzzled by a fine display of Very lights and searchlights to the north, later revealed to be the results of the French decision to scuttle their fleet in the face of the German invasion of the 'Unoccupied Zone', and the following night they were treated to a similar vision when the R.A.F. bombed Turin. 'It was almost like the Northern Lights.'

Then, on the evening of November 30th, the submarine surfaced about 500 yards offshore and within the curve of the bay partly enclosed by Cape Mele, and Livingstone and Weatherall climbed down into their folboat and paddled slowly away over the quiet water. There was far too much light for Livingstone's peace of mind for starlight in those parts is a very real thing, and every dip of the paddles produced a whirl of green flame, with floating sparks flashing in ripples from the bow.

They landed on a narrow, shell-covered beach and pulled the boat first into the shadow of a low bank – but this was unsufficient to hide the boat from the main road, which they found to their disgust ran along only a few feet away. Their feeling of exposure was not lessened in any way when they glanced out to sea and realised that *Ursula* was still there sitting brazenly in the middle of the bay, visible to anyone who might pass along the road and apparently prepared to wait there until their own return – timed for 2330, half an hour before the moon would rise to shed yet more light upon an already spectacularly visible scene.

Just across the road, however, was a white wall with arches and a pair of tall wrought-iron gates leading into what appeared at first sight to be a cemetery. The gates proved to be wired up and Livingstone could hear voices coming from a house about eighty yards away inside the walls, but the area undoubtedly offered shelter amid its shadowed cypresses and poised statues so he cut the wire, and then, having waited while a group of people strolled past along the road (without, apparently, noticing *Ursula*), he and Weatherall ran the folboat quickly across and into the garden. Fortunately the gates did not squeak.

Exploration through the garden quickly convinced them that there was no way out on the far side, so somewhat reluctantly they went back through the gates and out onto the road, along which they then walked into the outskirts of the small town of Laigueglia. There they soon found a narrow path leading up between two small houses into a close, surrounded by cottages from which lights and voices issued.

They made their way cautiously between the cottages and on through the gardens at the back, trampling ruthlessly over vegetable plots and getting tangled in a vine trellis, clambered over a highly unstable rockery and narrowly avoided upsetting a row of dustbins – and to their relief and astonishment found themselves practically standing on the railway track. A tunnel mouth yawned blackly at them from 100 yards away, and they even found a garden bench upon which to sit while they made the final connection to the rather complicated series of charges they intended to use.

Quite soon they saw the tunnel mouth begin to illuminate, then, as they threw themselves to the ground, a train came swishing out of the tunnel and roared its way past them. As they picked themselves up and began to walk towards the tunnel, they suddenly heard a scrabbling sound and realised that there was a sentry somewhere in front. Hastily they dived into a bush and considered the situation with some alarm. It seemed impossible that the sentry could not have seen or heard them – a suspicion strengthened when a few moments later he shouted towards them and was answered from beyond them down the line. Then the door of a house about twenty yards away opened and someone came out and stood looking vaguely in their direction, while two lorries ground to a halt in the road quite near but out of sight.

Thoughts of hand-to-hand combat, silent struggles in the night, undignified capture and long months in prison camps flitted through their minds, but little or no movement seemed to be taking place, and it gradually dawned upon them that the tone of the remarks which were being exchanged was decidedly jocular. The sentries and the civilian were in fact chatting idly between themselves and seemed totally unaware of any hostile presence.

But by just being there the three Italians inhibited all movement, and it was nearly an hour before the first sentry was at last left on his own, idly chucking stones down on to the line from a position above the tunnel mouth. It was obviously impossible for them to stalk and kill him in the time left, and there was therefore no way for them to get into the tunnel itself, so the two men now moved about 150 yards down the line to a place where it curved quite sharply and there decided to plant their charges. Weatherall unpacked the material from the rucksacks and passed it to Livingstone, who scooped out the loose ballast under the tracks, then placed the charges and blocked up the switches under the rail so that they would make contact when a train went over.

At last it was all done. For good measure, Livingstone attached two 'clams' to posts carrying the overhead wires, but much time had now passed and they had to hurry in case they missed their rendezvous with the submarine at 2330. They trampled their way back down to the road – again through cottage vegetable gardens, again clambering over rockeries and low walls, again nearly strangling themselves on vine trellises – and at last reached the side of the road, but now found themselves separated from it by an enormous wire fence.

Fortunately no one came along as they cut their way through, but with time running ever shorter they had no alternative but to walk openly along the road, trusting to the anonymity of their khaki overalls, woolly caps, beards, darkened faces and general aspect of potential belligerence – for Livingstone was one of those burly men who look short and pudgy until one gets close enough to realise that they stand over six feet tall and weigh thirteen stone, all of it, in Livingstone's case, bone and muscle.

In the event, they met one Italian soldier who stared rather suspiciously at them until his eyes met Livingstone's glare at which a far more amicable expression quickly spread over his face, and two civilians who took no notice of them despite the fact that Livingstone had been whistling *The Ride of the Valkyries* until they were nearly abreast of him, when he suddenly, and he thought tactfully, switched to the overture *William Tell*.

The two were back at the garden by 2315, and in the folboat and paddling by 2325 (it was fortunate for all concerned that no one passed as they ran the boat down the beach, since at that point they would have taken extreme measures against interference), steering by Jupiter and flashing the R.V. signal as specified. As they approached the *Ursula*, her bulging bow with luminous water streaming through the row of holes in her plating as she rose and sank on the swell made her look exactly like some huge whale – but a welcoming and hospitable one.

Within minutes they were back aboard, the folboat stowed, the submarine turning and sliding out from the shore. Just before midnight, the expected happened: a train came out of the tunnel, and from his position on the bridge Livingstone saw a vivid flame shoot up behind the houses, followed by a succession of white electric flashes and then abrupt darkness as strings of lights on each side of the explosion went out. Seconds after, the noise came booming across the water to them; there was no doubt that success had crowned their efforts, though to what extent they would have to wait and see.

This they were able to do during the next four days, as *Ursula*'s captain, perhaps inspired by his passengers' success, decided to remain in the area and endeavour to pick off by shell-fire some of the Italian rolling stock. His first attempt took place two nights later, just before midnight, at a place only twenty miles from the scene of the previous exploit.

The train, unconscious of its danger, came on unsuspectingly. Really, it was extraordinarily like trying to pot a running hare. There is only time for three or four shots and if the engine is not hit it will escape. As it emerged from the tunnel, Marshall let drive. The shell missed the engine by about six feet, and it burst against the bank beyond the line, so that the first intimation the driver could have had must have been a sudden explosion close beside him. I think splinters must have whizzed around him but the only obvious result was that the lights went out and the train speeded up with a jerk. The next two shots were over, bursting against the hill behind, but the fourth hit the train amidships somewhere, without unfortunately stopping it. A final parting shot hit the line and produced a shower of dazzling sparks, but the train got away and, knowing that no more could be expected that night, we headed out to sea, leaving a sullen flicker of fire beside the tunnel where the first shell had lit the grass. The peace of the night was unbroken, no one seemed interested.[2]

The episode put an end for the time being to all rail traffic along that particular stretch of line; even the trains which had waited during the previous two days, blocked on each side of the damage caused by Livingstone and Weatherall, now withdrew to the main stations, out of range of *Ursula*'s gun.

But the adventures of the cruise were by no means over, for they also stopped, ransacked and finally blew up with her own depth-charges an Italian anti-submarine schooner (her crew had deserted her and rowed off into the darkness within minutes of the first shot), and later they returned to the coast near Oneglia and shelled an olive oil refinery, rupturing the tanks and felling a tall chimney.

Finally, on the way back to Gibraltar they caught the 2,000-ton S.S. *Marguerite II* sailing in ballast from Marseilles to Naples, took the captain and chief engineer aboard and sent the rest of the crew away towards the nearest land, after which *Ursula*'s first lieutenant and Livingstone went aboard to head the search party and for Livingstone to place charges. They found quantities of excellent charts, old log-books, some good navigational instruments, quite a lot of good-quality bulk food (no Chianti, alas), two Nazi ensigns and a small, shivering mongrel dog who later became the pet of the *Maidstone*.

It then became Livingstone's unenviable job to decide where to place charges to sink her, and eventually it was decided that the forward hold would provide the best place.

No.1 went to clear everyone off and I went down to prospect with my blue torch slung round my neck. I reached the bottom and found myself in a vast cavernous space like the inside of a barn, with thick dust on the floor and quite warm from the engines next door. The ship had a list to starboard and half the floor was covered with water about 18″ deep. There was a heavy silence except for an occasional echoing boom as the submarine bumped alongside, and a thin splash of water spouting through a leak in the bulkhead. It was an eerie place. No.1 lowered a 25lb. box of ammonal down to me, and I went around to find a good place for it, eventually jamming it up in the angle between the bulkhead and the ship's side. I could just see No.1's face at the far end, forty feet above me, peering through the opening at the top of the ladder. When everyone was off he called out to me, and I started the 10″ time mechanism, after which in an access of nerves, I proceeded to beat all records up the ladder.[3]

A quarter of an hour later they all observed the explosion from half a mile away and watched for a while as S.S. *Marguerite II* settled by the bows; then they turned and started for Gibraltar. Passing Ibiza, they received orders to proceed instead to Algiers, which annoyed them all, as had they known that would be their destination they could have put a prize crew aboard the *Marguerite* and taken her in. It would then have been a profitable as well as a successful cruise, though they would have had to wait until the end of the war for their prize money.

Livingstone and Weatherall were to return to the U.K. soon after the completion of the *Ursula* cruise, where they rejoined the 2nd S.B.S. training in England for the Far East, and thus remained outside David Stirling's organisation – the only 'Private Army' to do so, for by the end of 1942 even the L.R.D.G. were being co-opted into ever closer ties with the

S.A.S. Stirling was now casting his net enormously wide, for in addition to his raids forward into Tunisia (which, incidentally, were intended to link up with patrols from 2nd S.A.S. to be formed and commanded by his brother) and the formations training under Sutherland and Langton back at the eastern end of the Mediterranean, yet another formation was growing further east in Persia.

This had been brought into being by the same strategic factors which had given Sutherland, Langton and Newby their pleasant interlude on the Syrian coast the previous June: the danger of Russian collapse in the Caucasus, and the threat of a drive by Kleist or von Manstein down towards the crucial oil-fields around Abadan. This matter had so exercised the mind of General Sir H. Maitland Wilson, Commander-in-Chief, Persia and Iraq, that as early as September he had enquired about the possibility of an S.A.S. formation being made available for operations in the area, and the following month Stirling had sent Fitzroy Maclean to Baghdad to pursue the subject.

Maclean, it will be remembered, was the linguist who had accompanied Stirling on the Benghazi raid in May and who had had occasion to upbraid some of the Italian sentries for slovenly behaviour, but Italian was by no means his only foreign language. During the Thirties he had held Foreign Office posts in Paris and Moscow and was one of the very few people who had travelled widely in the Soviet Union (watched with some anxiety and bewilderment by various lower grade K.G.B. officials), and one of the even fewer Westerners who had been to both Bokhara and Samarkand before the war.

He had escaped from the confines of the Foreign Office when war broke out by suddenly evincing a desire for a political career, then immediately joined his father's old regiment, the Cameron Highlanders, as a private. Pursuit by an indignant Foreign Office eventually forced him to fight a by-election in the Conservative cause, which, despite the probability of his prolonged absence from England thereafter, he had won, thus giving Mr. Churchill the occasion to introduce him much later to President Roosevelt as 'the young man who used the Mother of Parliaments as a private convenience!'

During the latter part of October, therefore, Maclean travelled briskly through the countryside around Teheran, enjoying again the clear light and pure dry air of Central Asia and visiting the British troops stationed there. As most of them were thoroughly bored by months of inaction he found an abundance of volunteers from whom to make his choice, and could thus set high and exact standards – so exact indeed that it was later pointed out that some ninety per cent of his enrolment were born north of the Border.

He was about to set up camp and commence training when he was abruptly summoned to Teheran for a conference with Maitland Wilson's chief of staff, at which he found himself saddled with the task of kidnapping the Persian general commanding native forces in the Isfahan area, General Zahidi – for it had become evident that the man had made contact with the German High Command in the Caucasus – and spiriting him away to Palestine *en route* to even further distant places.

The story of this escapade has been well told in Maclean's own memoirs and has no place in detail in this history – except that for its fulfilment Maclean obtained use of a platoon of Seaforth Highlanders, many of whom remained with him when he returned to the training area, thus increasing yet further the Caledonian concentration. This was by no means a disadvantage, of course, for atavism is still a force to be reckoned with; and if Jocks in drink can display a frightening capacity for violence, they do the same on the battlefield, towards which they can also carry heavier loads greater distances than most. Scots were always to make up a high proportion of the operational strength of raiding formations, a proportion almost equalled by Irishmen from the Republic.

Throughout the closing weeks of 1942, therefore, Maclean exercised his new command in the mountains on and around the Iranian plateau, while Sutherland was similarly occupied in Syria. But at the end of the year, as Eighth Army fought its way towards Tripoli, General Wilson was ordered to leave Baghdad and take over the Middle East Command in Cairo, and both Sutherland and Maclean realised that this move might presage changes in emphasis and employment. Maclean extracted first a promise that his men would be transferred to

General Wilson's new command, and then permission to move them to Palestine where they would be nearer the next probable scene of operations.

He was in the process of organising the move, and Sutherland was bringing his men out of the mountains to Beirut to commence the seaborne part of their training, when suddenly they received the most alarming news. David Stirling had been taken prisoner near the Gabes Gap and within a few days of being identified by his captors had been flown to a prison camp in Italy. Africa was not to see him again until after the war.

It is not putting the case too strongly to say that with the disappearance of David Stirling from the scene which he had dominated for so long, chaos descended. At the time of his capture he effectively controlled three distinct formations: 1st S.A.S. Regiment including the 1st S.B.S., the French S.A.S. Squadron and the Greek Sacred Squadron – in all comprising 83 officers and 570 other ranks, and with an agreed establishment at least 50 per cent higher.

This entire organisation had been built up by Stirling himself and owed much of its success to his own imagination and forethought, but by its very nature it had attracted to it the kind of person who wished to have as little to do with administration or bureaucracy as possible. For instance, to those who knew him it was almost impossible to envisage Stirling's chief lieutenant, Paddy Mayne, sitting behind a desk dealing with paperwork – even the barest minimum necessary for an efficient organisation – so Stirling had had to do it himself and almost single-handed. Some of it he had tried to offload by bringing in older officers from regular regiments, but they were either recalled soon to their own battalions (sometimes at their own request), or else they succumbed to the atmosphere of the S.A.S., smuggled themselves on to operations and thereby defeated the object of their recruitment.

The need for security – the 'need to know' – had also contributed to a compartmentalisation which led to few people knowing what others in the same squadron – sometimes even in the same section – were engaged upon at

any particular moment. In the end it came down to the fact
that David Stirling was the only person who knew exactly
where everyone was supposed to be and what their purpose
there was, and what were the plans for their future
employment. It is arguable, of course, that with all this
knowledge locked inside his head he should never have run the
risk of being taken prisoner; but had he been the kind of man
who accepted such limitations, he would not also have been
the man to inspire loyalty in others, the vast majority of whom
by nature regarded all forms of authority with scepticism and
that wielded from behind a desk with contempt.

Confusion therefore reigned at Kabrit during February and
March, 1943, and it took two months of head-scratching
perplexity and a continuous turn-around of frustrated officers
and bewildered clerks before any pattern at all emerged from
the chaos. Men would arrive unannounced from
reinforcement centres; patrols would report in from
operations carried out as far afield as Tabarca or the Fezzan
about which only their leader and Stirling had had the
slightest knowledge; weapons, ammunition or vehicles would
suddenly be delivered by taciturn R.A.S.C. drivers with no
interest but to have the requisite forms signed so that they
could return from whence they came; messages, signals or
letters would arrive out of the blue in respect of matters with
which no one but Stirling and the senders had been
concerned, and no one now knew their relevance. And when a
very high personage indeed rang up S.A.S. headquarters with
an enquiry upon a very confidential matter and there was
nobody in the entire organisation who had the slightest idea of
what he was talking about, it became obvious that Draconian
measures were necessary.

Temporarily, the 1st S.A.S. disappeared, to be divided into
two different formations, each with a separate and distinct
area of operations. Stirling's original force, grouped around
the nucleus he had garnered from Layforce and now under
command of the redoubtable Paddy Mayne, would be
reformed under the name Special Raiding Squadron and in
due course move westwards and operate ahead of the Eighth
Army in Tunis, and later in Italy.

The units in the eastern Mediterranean would for the
moment stay there, retaining the beige beret and insignia of

the Special Air Service and also the operational targets traditional to the S.A.S. – bridges, roads, barracks, airfields etc. As, however, these would for the most part be situated on islands scattered through the Aegean and eastern Mediterranean and must therefore first be approached across the sea, the new formation would revert to an old name; it would be called the Special Boat Squadron. It would consist of three detachments, each with an establishment of seventy men and seven officers – S Detachment commanded by Captain Sutherland, L Detachment commanded by Captain Langton, and M Detachment commanded by Captain Maclean. The squadron itself would be commanded by Major the Earl Jellicoe, would begin its official existence on April 1st, and establish its first base at Athlit, south of Haifa, where a long stretch of golden sand terminated at the foot of a Crusader castle.

All memories of the spring and early summer of 1943 at Athlit are of high spirits, of days spent tramping energetically over the thyme-scented sides of Mount Carmel, splashing happily through the surf in or out of folboats or cruising offshore in caiques under the eagle but indulgent eye of Ken Lamonby. There was ample space for those who wished or needed to increase their proficiency with sniper's rifle or Tommy-gun, the rations were varied and well-cooked, and there was a local café in the village where every mortal thing including food and drink was sold.

Above all there was a feeling of excitement and exhilaration, heightened by a sober realisation that these halcyon days were but a preparation for periods – perhaps extended – of danger and acute discomfort from which some would return in pain and others not return at all. As John Verney was to write much later,

We were there by our own fervent wish, and were free to leave any time we chose. No one tried to parade his authority – there was very little of that sort of authority to parade. Nor was there much place for the detestable concept of one-upmanship. There was no point in pretending, for example, that you could swim better than you did, when your capacity was tested daily and exposed, and when – the vital point – there was no advantage to

be gained by that or any other similar pretence. We pretty soon
came to know one another's physical and mental capacities, and
with them our own. Strength and skill were respected, and a fair
degree of both were essential, but everyone recognised that there
were other qualities, such as a cool head, or a good temper, that
might well prove more valuable. On our type of operation the
man who could make you laugh was more worth while having
than the bore who could only shoot straight.[4]

This was the attitude of the man who was acting as
adjutant, and it undoubtedly reflected the point of view of the
majority. Jellicoe himself at this time was only twenty-five
years of age, 'brown as a nut, with a nose like the Iron Duke's,
and an extensive capacity for irony.' But it was a capacity
rarely used within the confines of the camp – so long, of
course, as everyone worked with a will – being reserved for
outsiders who did not understand either the uses or the
limitations of Special Service units, or for newcomers who
disagreed with his principles of training.

These were certainly unorthodox to some degree. There
was little or no attempt at parade-ground discipline – it is
difficult to stamp to rigid attention on sand – and the very fact
that most of the daylight hours and many of those of darkness
were spent in hard physical activity in conditions dominated
by sun, sand and sea meant that the participants were often
dressed in nothing but shorts or trunks and sometimes not
even in those. But discipline there undoubtedly was – of the
more testing sort, for it was self-imposed; and those who failed
to apply it were quickly subjected to the only punishment the
unit knew: to be R.T.U'd., returned to unit, banished from the
company of those who chose to fight their war away from the
orthodox constraints – and protections, for there are several –
of normal battalion life.

Obviously, with so high a degree of individuality in so small
a compass there were differences of opinion. Fitzroy
Maclean's M Detachment when it arrived showed a
predilection for the emblems and insignia of military life
which excited a certain amount of derision at first among the
other detachments. But although inter-detachment rivalry
was quite keen, it never became bitter, restricting itself to
jocularity but not animosity. And all detachments would unite

solidly against outside criticism, as many a too-thick-skinned recruit of whatever rank quickly found.

A very large proportion of both officers and men who joined the S.B.S. at this time forfeited rank to do so, captains dropping to lieutenants, sergeants to corporals and corporals back to privates; but few regretted it if they stayed, and they presumably regained their ranks if they didn't. The ones who stayed formed a catholic yet eclectic company, each individual contributing differently to the general talent and expertise of the group.

Not that all contributions were appreciated. One of the newcomers, Philip Pinckney, who had taken part in many of the raids on the French coast by home-based commandos, was a naturalist by inclination, and he and John Verney suggested to Jellicoe that knowledge of edible flora and fauna might in some circumstances spell the difference between survival and surrender. With Jellicoe's encouragement the two spent days collecting and experimenting with nettles, dandelions, unidentified roots and even snails, slugs and grass snakes, producing at the end a concoction which they christened 'Palestine Soup'. They and Jellicoe pronounced it excellent and had second helpings, and most of the other officers strove manfully to clear their plates though one groped for the whisky bottle after the first mouthful and left hurriedly. As it turned out, even that one mouthful must have had dire effects, for only Jellicoe escaped a most uncomfortable night. Evidently a successful commander's stomach followed his dictates as obediently as did his subordinates.

But the idea of living off the land was too pragmatic a concept to be allowed to fail without further trial, and when training his patrol, Pinckney persisted in trying to keep them all going on the local vegetation. Only his own charm and evident sincerity saved him from an occasional mutiny, and none of these or other well meant attempts at providing food, either from the local environment or in easily portable form, could overcome the British soldier's fondness for meat and potatoes. Even later, when the American K rations became available, they were not regarded with much favour. 'What we want is bulk!' was the comment of one S.B.S. corporal, gloomily surveying the mixture of cereals, boiled sweets, coffee extract and Spam which was his own garnering from the waxed paper boxes the patrol had been carrying for days.

Another notable newcomer to Athlit was Captain Walter Milner-Barry, who had been a Shell-Mex official in Aden and Palestine before the war and on its outbreak had secured a commission in the Trans-Jordan Frontier Force. He had been attached to the Greek forces who had escaped from their country after the German invasion – as liaison officer, on the strength of a very shaky command of their language – and then personally to Colonel Tsigantes when the latter decided to form the Greek Sacred Squadron, or 'Eros Lokos', named after the band of Spartans who had fought to the last man at Thermopylae against the Persians.

Milner-Barry was somewhat older than the general run of S.B.S. officers, and his pre-war experiences had given him a maturity and resultant diplomatic charm which was to be put to good use. Twentieth-century Greeks have not all inherited the philosophic attitudes of Pericles, and at the beginning the Sacred Squadron consisted in large part of officers who had been willing to serve in the ranks in such a patriotic cause, but who were unwilling off the parade-ground to give up the perquisites and standing of officers – officers, moreover, in fashionable regiments with rather more class distinctions than were found among the British Special Forces, with which the Sacred Squadron was closely integrated. In time Greeks and S.B.S. became close friends and the friendship was sealed by dangers shared and mutual losses suffered, but in spring, 1943, suspicion and dislike existed on both sides. Their gradual disappearance owed much to Milner-Barry's diplomacy.

This was needed even more urgently in May of that year to deal with outraged naval and military authority on Cyprus. Milner-Barry and a patrol including both Shaun O'Reilly (who proved to be an exceptionally good cook) and Langton's companion from Tobruk, Private Watler, had taken passage to Cyprus on the schooner *Apostolos*, under charter and still with her Greek captain and some of her crew aboard. Once there, they intended to carry out a training-exercise involving a clandestine landing, a long march towards an inland objective, re-supply and reinforcements dropped to them by parachute, followed by a mock attack on the objective and a tactical withdrawal and pick-up on the coast.

Unfortunately, knowledge of the exercise did not reach the relevant authorities in Cyprus in time. The *Apostolos* was as a result fired upon shortly after Milner-Barry and his men had left her, and the ship was boarded, the captain arrested, and some days later Milner-Barry and his men were surrounded and caught near Nicosia after a stream of frantic signals had been issued by the local corps commander. Milner-Barry talked his way successfully out of the problem at the hurriedly assembled Court of Inquiry, but some days later, on the way back to Haifa, he and his party found themselves again the recipients of unwanted attentions, and this time his eloquence could not avail.

Sea calm, and progress slow. At about 1045, just as we were prepared to wireless H.Q., two aeroplanes appeared from nowhere and bombed us from 3,000 feet. Thought, at first, they were ours making a mistake, but somebody recognised Capronis. Ordered guns on deck, without any clear plan, but then was told that the Greeks had baled out in the dinghy, and Cass, observing this, dived after them, followed by Laverick, Fletcher and Kingsbury. This left me with O'Reilly, Watson, Geddes and Donnachie, the last two unable to swim properly. Not enough men to launch Goatley, I thought, so prepared to lower folboat. Whilst we were doing this, the bombers came back and dropped two more sticks, much closer this time. This treatment stimulated us to get the folboat away with Geddes and Donnachie, and Watson to look after them, but there had been no time to repair the boat after the scheme, and it promptly filled and capsized.

However, Geddes and Donnachie clung to it, so they were all right. Then O'Reilly dived overboard and I followed him, leaving *Apostolos* empty, but with sails up and engine running. The bombers came back a third time, but again missed, though the boat was shaken. They next came round, three or four times, and machine-gunned her with incendiaries, hitting her on the water-line, and on deck, but failing to set her on fire.

Watson and I both attempted to swim back to the boat when the planes had gone, but they came back so we had to push off quick, diving under the water when the bullets came. I don't think they were aiming for us but we weren't taking chances. Fortunately the water was calm and warm, and everyone was cheerful.

At last the bombers disappeared, and we tried to catch the boat which was chugging round in a wide circle, the tiller having jammed, by the Grace of God. Watson got almost alongside but was washed off, and I got within 10 yards, but we were beginning to think we were in for a long wait, when the rowing boat with the Greeks reappeared and by masterly judgement caught the *Apostolos*.[5]

Two more false alarms brought them almost to the point of diving overboard again that day, and the next morning the sight of a long grey shape circling the boat gave them all a nasty turn but, submarine or huge fish, it departed in due course, and *Apostolos* eventually reached Beirut safely, their crew and passengers tired but very thoughtful. Shortly afterwards *Apostolos* was bought by the Royal Navy and became officially a part of the ever-growing fleet of miscellaneous craft allotted to Raiding Forces.

The most notable addition to the complement of the Special Boat Squadron at this time was undoubtedly Anders Lassen.

Lassen was a Dane who at the outbreak of war had found himself stranded in England, a country for which he had great affection. Despite his pre-war occupation as a cadet in his country's merchant marine he had no particular fondness for the sea, and after Dunkirk he joined the British Army and in the glorious summer of 1940 found himself training with one of the early commandos up in the west of Scotland. Here his innate military talents were quickly recognised: his extraordinarily quick reflexes and his ability to move over ground so smoothly and quietly that he seemed hardly to touch it – both qualities supremely demonstrated when on one occasion he stalked and captured a stag, killing it with a knife.

Not surprisingly he was chosen for one of the first operations calling for commando skills: the penetration of Vichy French waters off the West African coast, close to Dakar, where three German merchantmen were lying. The party attacked the ships under cover of darkness, found them manned by skeleton crews and so captured them, sank two of the ships and sailed the third back to Britain. On the way back, the commander of the little force, Captain Gus March-Phillips, noticed that Lassen was still a lance-corporal whilst all other members were officers.

'I think we'd better have you commissioned, Andy,' he

announced, and within a few weeks Lassen had put up his first pip. Few such instant appointments have proved so eminently worthwhile.

Lassen spent some time training fifty of his fellow-countrymen (including his own brother) in commando techniques, and most of them were eventually parachuted back into Denmark to help organise and run the underground there, but by this time Lassen himself was back with No.62 Commando, taking part in raids on the French coast and the Channel Islands. With him on some of these raids had been Philip Pinckney, and by the end of 1942, certain names had become so well known to the German authorities in Paris that it was decided to disband the Commando and disperse its better-known characters. Brigadier Laycock, now back in England commanding the 1st Special Service Brigade, had not forgotten his Layforce days, so Pinckney and Lassen joined S.B.S. at Athlit almost as a gift from an old friend.

Lassen joined David Sutherland's detachment, attended one of the mountain warfare courses up in the Lebanon and impressed Sutherland and indeed everyone he met with his shrewd common sense, his undoubted talents and experience in raiding operations, and his immense personal charm when he cared to exert it. Not that this was immediately appreciated by all, one very highly-regarded N.C.O. proving especially resistant to it – though it must be said that the resistance did seem to have its origins in a general xenophobia. Lassen observed the phenomenon quietly for some time until it became obvious that only drastic measures would have any lasting effect, then one evening both of them disappeared and were not seen again for some hours.

What exactly happened must remain a matter of conjecture, but it was observed upon their return that they both seemed extremely cheerful, that Lassen had a split and swollen lip as did the N.C.O., who in addition developed a spectacular black eye during the following morning. He had also apparently shed his anti-Danish attitude, for from then on he was always one of the first to volunteer to accompany Lassen on operations, even of the most dubious practicability.

By May the days of the Panzerarmee in North Africa were

numbered, and it was becoming evident that very soon the Allies would be mounting operations against what Mr. Churchill referred to as 'the soft underbelly of Europe'. Obviously probing attacks and reconnaissance raids on Sicily, Italy and Greece must precede any large-scale landings, and equally obviously, these should take place at widely divergent localities so as not to divulge the real aim of Allied tactics.

To the S.B.S. detachments waiting at Athlit, the receipt of orders from Raiding Forces H.Q. to prepare and brief teams for operations on Crete, Sardinia and Sicily came as something of a relief, for training had reached a pitch when fitness was passing its peak and repetition threatened boredom and consequent loss of morale. David Sutherland's men were the first to move, their objectives being three of the airfields on Crete which had been raided the year before – Heraklion, Kastelli and Tymbaki – and on June 22nd, almost exactly a year after the previous visit to the island, Sutherland himself and two patrols sailed for a landing beach near Cape Kokinoxos.

Orders for *Operation Albumen* stated quite clearly that the primary task for all patrols was the destruction of enemy aircraft, such alternative targets as petrol or bomb dumps being attacked only if it appeared that this was the best way to destroy nearby planes, or if they offered the only practicable target. The orders also stated categorically that Sutherland's job would be to remain near the landing-point and organise a base area from which patrols would be despatched to the three targets, the patrols themselves being commanded by junior officers – Lieutenants Lamonby, Lassen and Rowe. Each patrol would include a signaller, and somehow his W/T set and battery, together weighing some 65 lbs., would be carried in addition to the weapons, food, explosive and miscellaneous equipment necessary for both the task and for survival.

By 0115 hours on the morning of June 23rd, Sutherland, Lamonby and Lassen were ashore with their men and equipment, and the H.D.M.L. which had brought them was burbling off back into the darkness. Rowe's patrol would be landed four days later.

All equipment not immediately required was hidden among boulders at the rear of the beach, after which the whole party moved out through the narrow and precipitous gorge

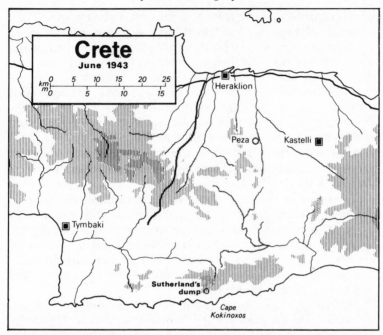

which constituted the only exit. Owing to the weight each man was carrying – 70 to 80 lbs. per man – the quite appalling nature of the country they were crossing, and, inevitably, the uncertainty of the guides, they did not reach the lying-up area until after first light and thus had to move with great circumspection during the rest of the first day.

Small caves were found in the sides of a wadi, a water-point was found only half a mile away, positions of command over all approaches were surveyed, and the decision taken that Lassen and Lamonby should start out during the late afternoon so as to cover at least a part of the atrocious going in daylight. In order to spare them some exhaustion, Sutherland took a small party back to the beach at midday and brought up rations for them and the two essential batteries for the W/T sets, already the cause of some speculation and a considerable amount of bad language.

The two patrols duly marched out and they remained together for the first five nights, making slow and arduous progress over rock-strewn hills and along tortuous gullies which strained their muscles and drained their strength. Their only consolation was the friendliness and co-operation of all the Cretans they met, who not only provided food and water and even occasionally helped with the loads, but also gave them up-to-date information on local conditions and the probabilities of running into enemy troops. It was quite obvious that if the natives had been as hostile as the environment, the patrols would never have reached their targets, let alone been able to attack them.

As it was, the night after the two patrols had split up, Lamonby's party were sheltered and guided by a colonel of the Greek Army who had himself been in hiding since the fall of the island in 1941; he also gave them valuable contacts for the next crucial stage. This took them to within a night's march of their target, and they arrived there with two days to spare for rest and observation, infinitely aided in this by Greeks who worked in and around Heraklion airfield every day and who now came out and reported on the activity and conditions there in the evenings.

But though the information was valuable it was not welcome, for the news they brought was that Heraklion airfield had declined in importance to the Germans over the last year, having been run down, it seemed, as a result of Jellicoe's attack. Very few aircraft ever used the place and none ever stayed the night. Lamonby was also warned not to be fooled by a group of four planes on the far side of the drome, for they were dummies.

This news, of course, was extremely disappointing – though not so disappointing as the position found by Lieutenant Rowe when he and his men arrived above their target at Tymbaki. After a delayed landing and an arduous approach march which had so exhausted them all that they would have been totally unable to defend themselves if attacked, they arrived to find that the airfield had been completely out of use since the previous December.

In the circumstances, Lamonby decided that there was no point in moving closer to Heraklion, and changed targets. On the appointed D-day minus 1, he therefore moved to the slopes of a hill overlooking the village of Peza where he had been told there was a sizeable petrol dump, and during the afternoon sent the Greek guide dressed in civilian clothes borrowed from

the Greek colonel down to make a thorough reconnaissance of
the target.

The guide's report was satisfactory, and as soon as it was
dark the party descended from their hillside and slipped
across a main road to approach the valley in which lay the
dump, and there hid amid tangled vines to await the passing
of an officer and guard-dog due, according to their
guide, in twenty minutes' time. The guide had been right, and
half an hour after their arrival in the vines, he and Lance-
Corporal Holmes slid away along the bottom of a trench
which led into a clearing containing the nearer section of the
dump.

From the end of the trench, Holmes could see the piled
barrels. There were about fifty of them each containing sixty
gallons, and he and the guide worked their way along the
length of the rows, placing charges between every third pair.
They pressed the two-hour time pencils at 2315, and Holmes
was about to move back when he realised that the guide had
disappeared – but only temporarily, for then Holmes both
glimpsed and heard him as he made his way up a slight bank
back towards the vines. So, unfortunately, did a sentry, and
for some minutes Holmes was trapped in the shadows of the
dump, his discomfort much increased by the return of the
officer and dog. There is only one course to follow in such
circumstances and it is wholly a matter of self-control; dogs
can smell fear – or rather, the emanations which fear causes –
and rising panic will bring them charging towards their
quarry quicker than a bitch in heat. It was a cool but very
relieved lance-corporal who some minutes later rose to his feet
and made his way quietly back to the end of the trench,
hearing behind him the sentry, the officer and the dog moving
away towards other dumps at the far end of the clearing.

There Holmes found Lieutenant Lamonby, but no sign of
the guide – and as only the guide knew the exact positions of
the rest of the dump, Lamonby himself set off on
reconnaissance, telling Holmes and the rest of the men to move
back to the vines and find the guide.

The next hour was frustrating in the extreme. The guide
had disappeared, and presumably as a result of the noise he
had made, sentries were now closely guarding the dump
perimeter while others prowled between the rows of barrels. As

the raiders had to be at least across the road before the bombs started to go off, and preferably quite a way beyond, Lamonby reluctantly returned and gave orders to strew all remaining explosives around the area where they lay, and then to move off.

At 0110 the first charge exploded, and within minutes the whole of the surrounding countryside was lit by a giant fire. As the patrol fled back into the hills, more charges blew and split the nearby drums; petrol spread in flaming lakes which engulfed the entire dump, until all the drums were bursting through heat alone, adding to a holocaust which drove the sentries out of the area and away from the perimeter. Within minutes the lakes had flooded across to the parts of the dump outside the area of Holmes's activity, thus justifying Lamonby's decision not to press the attack into the heavily-guarded areas which in all contained some 50,000 gallons of petrol.

Soon the whole area was aflame and the valley resounded with explosions and the roar of flames, quickly added to by the scream of sirens as fire engines raced out from Heraklion.

It was a truly astonishing sight, and a sobering but also satisfying memory for Lamonby and his men as by D plus 1 they marched south across the mountains and plains of Crete, towards the rendezvous with Lassen and then the dump and embarkation point.

Lassen's patrol, in the meantime, had been experiencing the kind of hair-raising adventure which was soon to be recognised as the price to be paid for accompanying him into any kind of danger.

The patrol had arrived on time above the airfield at Kastelli – though the accompanying signallers had been left behind, as the loads they had been carrying had exhausted them almost to the point of collapse – and had spent a day observing and obtaining information from the ever-helpful local Cretans. The main target was a cluster of eight Stukas at the south-western corner of the field, and there were also five Ju.88s., a few fighters and some older planes dispersed elsewhere. The Cretans, however, were doubtful of the chances of success, especially against the Stukas for, they claimed, every one was guarded by three sentries working in shifts, plus an outer ring of guards surrounding the blast shelters, posted ten yards apart and specifically with their backs to the runways so that their attention was always on the planes. Within the ring were also situated the guard tents in which slept those off duty.

All this 'I considered to be an exaggeration' Lassen later wrote cryptically – but he nevertheless recast his plans. Instead of attacking through the area with his patrol concentrated, he would follow the example set at Rhodes by Sutherland and split his force – one half of which would cause as noisy and spectacular a diversion as possible. This would enable Sergeant Nicholson and Corporal Greaves to carry out the main purpose of the raid without too much interference, having been guided to their attack point by the Greek guide provided by M.O.4., Kimon Legonfakis.

The plan worked well, but with some interesting extensions. Nicholson and Greaves watched their sector for the whole of the afternoon before the attack and discovered that what the Cretans had said about sentries was substantially correct, but that in addition there was always at least one sentry on each taxi track. Air movement during the day had left a complement of seven Stukas in the blast shelters, but an extra Ju.88 came in to land as the two men started their approach march, and on cutting their way through the double-apron and Dannert fence, they found it parked only a few hundred feet away.

Moreover, while they were still actually cutting their way in, there had been a burst of automatic fire on the other side of the field which had so distracted the attention of the guards that the two had planted bombs on the Ju.88 within minutes. Beside the next plane along, however, were gathered three sentries obviously in conference regarding the recent sounds of action – which now seemed to have died down – so Nicholson and Greaves crept past them to the next plane, another Ju.88, which again they quickly decorated with explosive.

But now they were inside an area well populated with sentries and, although there were many excellent objectives within easy reach, it was only too obvious that any movement towards them would attract attention. While Nicholson was pondering this situation, chaos and confusion suddenly erupted in what was obviously Lassen's operational area, and his 'diversion' rapidly assumed the proportions of a minor battle.

Lassen and Gunner Jones had cut their way through the wire well before midnight and had walked openly along the taxi track in the direction of the Stukas, stopping at intervals to crouch down and observe, hoping to spot danger silhouetted against the sky or against the glare of a fire away on their left, around which about twenty Italians were sitting talking.

Satisfied that they had not been seen, Lassen stepped off the track towards the Stukas – despite the fact that they were really Nicholson's target and his approach might spell trouble – but was almost immediately challenged by a sentry standing in the shadows. Bluffing his way past him by pretending to be a German officer (the sentries were almost all Italians), Lassen went on his way with Jones behind him, to find that he had come up against the 'ring'; immediately he was challenged by another man, and bluffed him in the same way … and then another … and another.

But as he approached the fourth man, those behind apparently became suspicious and began shouting, at which point the fourth man came to the 'on guard' position. Lassen distracted his attention by pointing at the fire beyond him, then fired two shots into the unfortunate man's stomach, at which the sentries behind, plus others ahead, joined action, firing into the area in which they supposed their enemies to be. But both had gone, Jones having been suddenly inspired to emulate Lassen's incredible ability to drift rapidly and apparently invisibly from place to place as the situation demanded. Unfortunately for the Italians, however, their target area lay between themselves and their compatriots around the fire, and in less than a minute both groups were fighting each other, only saved from disaster by the darkness of the night and their own poor marksmanship.

By the time this particular local battle had died away, Lassen and Jones had slipped off to an area 'a little higher up where things appeared quiet, as a great commotion was going on in the area we had just left.' But here too, they soon found themselves surrounded by another ring of men and in the middle of an anti-aircraft battery – a situation which Lassen resolved by expert and copious use of grenades. He then moved to yet another area 'where everything was silent', and it remained so until he was challenged again, this time by a German sentry; again Lassen went up and 'disposed of him with my automatic.'

This was the signal for a very full diversion indeed. Very lights shot up, rifle and automatic fire cracked and chattered, to which Lassen and his accomplice replied with more grenades thrown from the shadows around a huge caterpillar tractor, upon which they then placed bombs before racing in a crouching run towards their escape route through the wire.

Meanwhile, Nicholson and Greaves were profitably occupied. As soon as they saw that sufficient attention had been attracted away from their own locality and into Lassen's, they moved swiftly. They put a bomb on the nearest Stuka, but were spotted by a lone sentry who fired at them as they ran towards the one they had by-passed before, driving them away into some trees. Here they found a petrol dump which they hastily garlanded, then crept back to the by-passed Stuka and placed a bomb on its tail despite the fact that sentries were standing by the wings watching the pyrotechnics out in the field. They were then forced away when a truck screamed up to disgorge a dozen men who scattered among the rest of the parked planes.

The two men withdrew towards the trees and were unexpectedly rewarded for their determination by finding another Stuka, so far unnoticed, which absorbed the remainder of their charges. As they crawled out through the hole in the wire where the highly excited Greek guide was still faithfully awaiting them, the first of the charges went off, and by the time they were clear of the area, six separate fires were blazing, trucks and fire engines were racing around the perimeter and across the field – and searchlights were playing across their only way out and over the hillside.

Nevertheless, within two hours they reached the lying-up area where they had left their kit and by dawn were safe in the mountains to the south. From there they made their way, protected and fed by the Cretans who passed them safely from village to village through the mountains, back to Sutherland's dump, where they arrived early on the morning of July 10th.

Lassen and Jones, however, had had by no means so

unopposed a passage.

Most exceptionally, they had been betrayed at some time during the first day of their withdrawal, and only the acute sensitivity to danger that was to keep Lassen alive for as long as it did saved them both now. Instead of dropping into a coma of exhaustion, which his activities during the previous hours – indeed days – might have warranted, Lassen was wide awake when the Germans began to search the area where he was lying up, and he and Jones dragged themselves into the nearby mountains and found a cave. Here they lay without moving and without food – though fortunately they had some water – for three and a half days, until their pursuers concluded they had got away and abandoned the search.

During the fourth night after the attack they reached the rendezvous with Lamonby's patrol, and three nights later the combined force reached the re-embarkation area and the presumed security of Sutherland's dump. But none of them was safe yet.

If Sutherland and the dump party had been spared the physical exhaustion of the overland marches, they had suffered instead the waiting strain and the boredom and discomfort of day-long watches over the approach routes. For the wireless operator there had also been the problem of keeping a continuous check on all signals traffic between the patrols and Cairo without, however, draining his batteries – and for Sutherland, the equally continuous strain of responsibility for the whole operation.

The first three days had been spent in organising the dump and assuring its safety, then on the night of June 27th/28th, the third patrol under Lieutenant Rowe had been successfully landed. Again, the heavy burdens to be carried by each man and the appalling nature of the ground to be covered delayed their arrival at the lying-up area, and this time the problem was further complicated by the fact that the whole patrol had been weakened by almost continual sea-sickness during the previous day. But they were in hiding by morning, and to give them as good a rest as possible, Sutherland and one of the dump party kept look-out during the day while others brought up the rest of the rations and the spare radio batteries from the beach.

At 2300 Rowe's patrol set off for the airfield at Tymbaki on what proved to be a totally fruitless mission, as has been reported, and Sutherland and his men returned to the main dump to take up again the monotonous tasks of keeping watch, and listening to and retailing the messages passed between the patrols and Cairo.

Then came D-day, and with it the anxiety of the dark hours when all knew that close friends were venturing into extreme danger from which luck must play a large part in sheltering them, then the long, tense wait for the first news. This came in the late afternoon of D plus 1, signifying success at Kastelli and Heraklion but nothing worthy of attack at Tymbaki. Then silence, until suddenly during the afternoon of D plus 3, a signal came in from Ken Lamonby warning of imminent enemy patrol activity in the coastal sector nearby.

By this time Rowe was back at his own dump, made despondent not only by all the wasted effort on the part of his patrol but also by a claim from his guide that another Greek had robbed them of 1,500,000 Greek drachma ('So he alleges,' Rowe's report states darkly). Sutherland visited him with the warning of possible danger and also the news that re-embarkation had been arranged for the night of July 11th/12th, and the following day Rowe visited the main dump so as to ensure efficient concentration upon it if necessary. That afternoon Sutherland's wireless operator told him that judging by the strength of messages sent out by Lamonby's patrol, they – and presumably Lassen's – must be less than ten miles away. Now only patience and luck were required to see them all safe.

Patience plus planning were sufficient to carry them through the next two days, despite one expected and two unexpected factors. As expected, the wireless batteries grew weaker and weaker, and only by fetching in the batteries from the outlying patrols and linking them in series could sufficient power be raised to confirm details for the pick-up. Unexpected was the news brought in by one of the M.O.4 agents that reprisals were being taken by the Germans for the raids and that it was possible that as many as fifty Cretans had already been shot. As a consequence, but equally unexpected was the realisation that twenty-five to thirty Cretans who had helped the patrols had now joined them, and were hoping to escape from Crete when Sutherland and his men left. They needed to be given hope on this point, and by midnight on July 10th Lassen's and Lamonby's men had closed in to the main dump, while the Cretans were concentrated in the gorge below, assured that every possible measure would be taken to help them.

Nicholson and Greaves had already arrived, and at first light on July 11th Rowe brought his men in with the news that an enemy patrol of one German and three Greek policemen were moving in from the west; but although extra guards were posted, no signs of enemy presence were seen throughout the morning and afternoon. At this point a problem began to develop with the Cretans. With everybody keyed up and the sun overhead, thirst affected all, and the Cretans could see no reason why they should not go in search of water. Quite severe measures had to be taken, the point of which was only appreciated when in the early evening, two German soldiers were seen making their way up the approach to the gorge.

Without a shot being fired they were ambushed and captured by men from Rowe's and Lassen's patrols, with Lamonby's men holding the Cretans back by force from the objects of their revenge; but while the two prisoners were being searched, two more Germans were seen at the bottom of the wadi, and 'being for once in their lives on more or less equal terms', the Cretans opened fire with their old rifles and shot-guns, and an almost total ignorance of tactics. The two Germans retired coolly and efficiently, keeping the Cretans at bay with sub-machine-gun fire and grenades – and with a great deal of noise, which was the last thing Sutherland wanted. By this time darkness was falling, the noise of the skirmishing could undoubtedly be heard for miles up and down the coast and would equally undoubtedly attract any other Germans in the area – and the rescuing M.L. might not arrive for another six hours.

In this predicament, Sutherland sent Ken Lamonby and four men out to quell the disturbance, which they did to such effect that most of the Cretans and the four men of the patrol were back at the dump by 2100, thus allowing Sutherland to organise the lift of personnel and equipment down to the beach at 2150. Once there, the prisoners were guarded by men of Rowe's patrol, the Cretans were disarmed of all guns, knives and sticks and marshalled at the rear of the beach under the Birettas of Lamonby's patrol, and all wireless sets and other equipment were laid out in six lines close to the water's edge.

But there was no sign of Lamonby, so Sutherland sent Lassen and two of his men to look for him – to no avail, alas, for Lamonby had acted with great courage but not sufficient thought.

It takes two and preferably three men properly to stalk and kill or capture two enemies, even if the quarry are not particularly well-trained – and these two Germans were both well-trained and expert. They were aware of the numbers who had first engaged them and who at the height of the action were pinning them amid the rocks on a steep hillside dropping to the sea. They had heard the shouting when Lamonby's men were bringing the Cretans under control and shepherding them away – and they guessed that someone had stayed behind to prevent their own rapid escape.

They therefore moved with care and skill up and down the hillside with one always covering the other during movement, and in due course they reaped the rewards of their efficiency. Ken Lamonby glimpsed a figure dodging between rocks, lifted himself out of cover to fire – and was seen and killed by the other. He was thus the only British casualty of *Operation Albumen*, but a grievous one and greatly missed.

In ignorance of what had happened, Sutherland concentrated upon the re-embarkation, which from then on went well. The M.L. was off the beach by 0015, close enough to allow the task of re-loading the stores to start five minutes later, and by 0105 everything and everyone was aboard and the M.L. was turning to sail slowly around the point of Cape Kokinoxos, to lie off the mouth of the wadi in which Lamonby had been last seen.

'There being no sign of him, the Captain set course for Matruh (0130 hrs.) which was reached at 1845 hrs. the following day, July 12th.'

Operation Albumen was over, and all that remained was the writing of the reports – and one other formality. On their way back through Cairo, Sutherland and Lassen felt thirsty, and as they were escorting the two prisoners they took them into Groppi's and stood them ice cream and coffee, reasoning that so many odd uniforms were to be seen there that surely two more would not be noticed. But they were – and reported. So Sutherland in due course received an official reprimand.

THREE

Dodecanese Disaster

JULY '43 – NOVEMBER '43

By the time Sutherland and his men were back from Crete, significant events were taking place elsewhere in the Mediterranean. On July 10th, 1943, *Operation Husky*, the Allied invasion of Sicily, had commenced, and as it was quite evident to the Italian people that the island's fall would inevitably be followed by an invasion of the mainland, their enthusiasm for the war – never very marked except in the minuscule circles of extreme Fascism – fell even further.

A week after the Allied divisions had gone ashore around the southern corner of the island, Mussolini had been haled by Hitler to an emergency meeting at Feltre, some fifty miles north of Venice, and on his way there Mussolini was urged in the strongest terms by his Chief of Staff, Generale Ambrosio, to tell Hitler that Italy could no longer prosecute the war and must ask the Allies for an armistice. In the event, Mussolini's nerve failed him, and his volatile nature reacted to Hitler's iron resolve to such an extent that after the meeting he defied Ambrosio and his other military advisers and threatened them with courts martial for pusillanimity. But while he and his German mentor had been in conclave in the north, 700 Allied planes had bombed Rome, severely damaged the marshalling yards and scattered thousands of leaflets over the capital, explaining to avid readers the dire state of Italian fortunes and the sympathy the Italian people could expect if they rid themselves of their present rulers and joined the Allied cause.

There followed a brief period during which Mussolini

invariably agreed with the last person he talked to, but the same
condition applied to any form of communication, even
imaginary; for although he eventually forced himself to draft a
letter to Hitler setting out the true position, he never summoned
up the courage to send it. When at last his ministers and
advisers realised that Il Duce would never break with Der
Führer, they decided they would have to take action
themselves. On the evening of July 24th a meeting of the Fascist
Grand Council was convened – the first since war had broken
out – at which military power was removed from Il Duce, and
the following day he was arrested; a new cabinet, containing
not a single member of the Fascist Party, was appointed, with
Marshal Badoglio at its head.

Twenty years of Fascism were at an end – but with
considerable German military presence throughout his
country Badoglio had obviously to move with care. He and the
whole Italian population wanted to get out of the war but were
realistic enough to know that there was a price to be paid, for
with Sicily already a battleground and Allied forces creeping
inexorably towards the Straits of Messina it was obvious that
the 'toe', if not the whole 'foot', of Italy would soon know the
horrors of war. What could be done to limit both the area of
devastation and its severity?

Obviously, the situation called for consummate diplomacy,
indeed delicacy; or, to put it more bluntly as Mr. Churchill
did, 'Badoglio knows that he is going to doublecross someone.
Let us ensure that it is the Germans, not us!'

The process began on the evening Badoglio took power
(July 25th), when he announced that he and his country
would continue the fight alongside their German comrades
until the Allies were beaten; at the same time he instructed the
Italian counsellor at the Lisbon embassy to make contact with
the British ambassador and suggest that the Allied
governments should not take this announcement too seriously.

This piece of Machiavellianism set the tone for the rest of
the month. During the days which followed there took place a
sequence of devious moves by all parties (including the
Germans, who had little doubt of the new Italian
government's real intentions), and as a result of these, coupled
with several Allied bombing raids on targets in southern Italy,
a 'short armistice' was signed in an olive grove near Syracuse

Dick Livingstone
and Ian Lapraik on
an S.B.S. training
exercise.

An S.A.S. patrol about to set out on an operation in the desert.

David Stirling, founder of the S.A.S.

The redoubtable
Paddy Mayne.

David Sutherland,
the indestructible
professional.

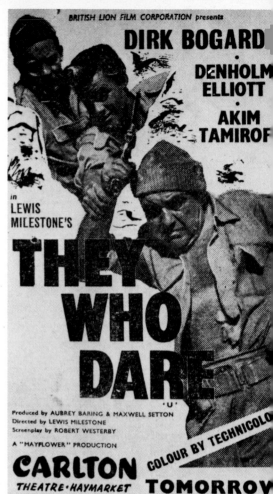

Poster for the film based on *Operation Anglo*, September 1942.

H.M. Submarine *Traveller*, which picked up Sutherland and Marine Duggan after the raid.

Shipping bombed in Grand Harbour, Malta.

S.B.S. convoy moving up to Athlit, April 1943.

Exit from the beach.

Beach on Crete where Sutherland, Lamonby and Lassen went ashore,
June 23rd, 1943.

Lassen and Lamonby, shortly before Lamonby was killed.

Jack Nicholson on Crete.

Assault Landing Craft (A.L.C.) used occasionally to take in patrols. Very sick-making!

Running repairs on the folboat.

on September 3rd, 1943.

Under its terms all Italian air and ground forces would lay down their arms when approached by Allied soldiers, the Italian fleet would sail for Malta, Allied prisoners of war in Italian hands would be released and in no circumstances allowed to fall into German hands, and all Italian territory *including the Mediterranean islands* would be made available to the Allies as operational bases from which to continue the war against the remaining European enemy. In return for this, the Allies were willing to guarantee 'kindly and sympathetic treatment' to the Italians, especially if Italian troops when they made contact with Allied troops co-operated fully against the now common enemy.

Although the Allies also promised not to announce the terms of this armistice for nine days, it was in fact made known on the evening of September 8th, thus causing a marked rise in military and political blood-pressure from Algiers up to Berlin and across to Washington, and a considerable fluttering of military hearts throughout the eastern Mediterranean.

Jellicoe on the evening of September 7th had been dining at the Hotel St. Georges in Beirut with a fellow officer, when their meal was interrupted by a Military Policeman who politely requested Jellicoe's immediate return to Raiding Forces H.Q. There he found orders to the effect that he was to fly to Cairo first thing on the morning of the 8th, and in the brief interval between – appreciating that some crisis was at hand – he motored quickly to Athlit to ensure that he knew the situation throughout his somewhat scattered command. During the preceding few weeks, even days, there had perforce been some changes.

Langton's health had lately deteriorated to such an extent that he had been invalided home, and his L Detachment, temporarily commanded by John Verney, had been attached to Raiding Forces at the other end of the Mediterranean for employment first in Sardinia and Sicily and then in Italy itself. Moreover, M Detachment was no longer commanded by Fitzroy Maclean, who had been suddenly translated by his linguistic ability and his Parliamentary standing from a captain commanding raiding troops to a brigadier representing British interests in general and Mr. Churchill's in particular, at the side of the Partisan leader Marshal Tito in the Yugoslav. mountains.

In his place Jellicoe had appointed J. Neilson (Ian) Lapraik, another ex-Cameron Highlander like Maclean, who had been one of the first men into Keren during the Abyssinian campaign of 1941 and had been awarded the ribbon of the Lion of Judah by Haile Selassie himself. Lapraik had also organised and run a commando training centre on one of the smaller islands off Malta, been wounded and taken prisoner near the Egyptian frontier during the great retreat, and had escaped as a result of a quite remarkable chain of events in which Rommel himself had played a significant part.

During a lull in the confused ebb and flow of battle at that time, the German commander had stopped his car alongside a group of British prisoners under guard and talked to some of them, including Lapraik. Noticing that he was wounded, Rommel gave orders that he should be given immediate attention, and at the nearest aid post, Lapraik to his astonishment found himself being bandaged by a pre-war German acquaintance. With perhaps mistaken warmth for his erstwhile friend, the German orderly so over-dressed Lapraik's wound (in the arm) that it assumed a far more serious appearance than was warranted with the result that instead of being despatched to a prison cage, Lapraik found himself *en route* to a hospital. From here without undue difficulty he escaped, then, of course, to face the long walk back to British lines at Alamein.

Jellicoe had met him during the late spring of 1943, and, realising that here was another small boat enthusiast, kept him in mind as a detachment commander should a vacancy arise. With Lapraik came also some of his comrades and colleagues from the training centre on Malta, including a New Zealander named 'Stud' Stellin, who possessed the curious distinction of having served at one time or another in all three services. Lapraik and Stellin and the others who came with him were all to play a significant part in the events which so quickly followed.

At Cairo H.Q. on the morning of September 8th, Jellicoe found himself amid a bewildering (and, one suspects,

bewildered) assortment of officers who, like himself, had only
the faintest idea of why they had been summoned. They were
quickly enlightened by a brigadier, who succinctly explained
to them that within a few hours an armistice with Italy would
be announced and that their immediate duty would be to
organise the despatch to Rhodes of a mission which would so
rally and encourage the Italian governor, his staff and the
troops of his command, that they would first contain and then
attack the German forces on the island. This would allow the
disembarkation of British troops sent to their assistance, the
rapid capture of Rhodes, and the subsequent domination of
the Aegean by R.A.F. planes based on those airfields attacked
by Sutherland and Allott a year before, at Calato and
Marizza.

There were, Jellicoe and the others were informed, some
35,000 Italians and 10,000 Germans on the island, but no one
was fooled by the disparity in numbers. Italian morale was
likely to be low, their deployment tactically unsound (the
Rhodes governor was an admiral), and their transport and
communications systems inefficient, whereas the German
equivalents would suffer no such handicaps. Moreover, such
was the lack of forewarning of the situation to the Middle East
Command, that the 'British troops' to be sent to assist in the
capture of Rhodes consisted of one infantry brigade (perhaps
4,000 men) which could not arrive before September 15th at
the earliest and would not be 'assault loaded'. It was therefore
essential that the Italians should secure control of either the
town and harbour of Rhodes and the nearby airfield of
Marizza, or, as a less satisfactory alternative, the village and
port of Lindos and its covering airfield at Calato.

It is hardly surprising that the assembled officers listened to
this exposition of the situation and the parts they were
themselves to play in its resolution with a degree of scepticism
– a scepticism which was both shared and then voiced by the
man who had been appointed to command the mission,
Colonel Turnbull, when eventually he arrived from Gaza
where he had been attending a Senior Officer's Course. There
was then yet another revelation to add to the air of unreality
which developed as the morning wore on, and this from the
Intelligence section.

There was, according to them, an M.O.4 representative on

Rhodes, who would be instructed to make immediate contact with Admiral Campioni, the Rhodes Governor, to warn him of the mission's imminent arrival. However, subsequent questioning revealed that no contact had as yet been made with the agent, who upon receipt of his instructions (in the form of a long, complicated message in code) would then be faced with the task of crossing some thirty miles of difficult country, obtaining an interview with the Admiral and convincing him not only of his *bona fides* but also of the acceptability of his suggestions. As the agent was a Greek peasant, the first part of his task might not prove totally impossible; but the odds on the successful completion of the second part seemed slim indeed.

So slim that Jellicoe suggested a radical alternative, which, after some discussion, was accepted. As a result, during the remainder of the afternoon and evening, messages flew between Cairo and Beirut, frantic talks took place over scrambled telephone lines, people scurried from office to office or raced in hurriedly summoned staff cars from headquarters to barracks or airfields and back again, and finally, just before dusk, two M.Ls. left Haifa under command of Lieutenant-Commander Frank Ramseyer, carrying between them two patrols from S Detachment under Milner-Barry and two from M Detachment under Captain J.S.F. 'Stewart' Macbeth – an officer recruited by Maclean, who combined a youthful appearance with a charm and suavity to match Milner-Barry's. Also on board were some surprised anti-aircraft gunners and some mysterious officials from an obscure political and Intelligence department, later joined by an R.A.F. signals detachment from Cyprus. David Sutherland was in command of the military section of the party, while Ian Lapraik was hurriedly collecting all the remainder of the S.B.S. in the area and organising them into a follow-up detachment. In all, the two parties would contain about fifty-five fighting men – which, even if they were strongly supported by Admiral Campioni and his men, was still not a large force to pit against 10,000 Germans.

But at least they might arrive soon.

Jellicoe himself arrived on Rhodes shortly before 2200 on the evening of September 9th, dropping out through the door of a Halifax bomber into a dark night, lit below by flashes of rifle fire directed at him and his two companions which, although inaccurate, was disconcerting.

Wind of unexpected force added to their difficulties, spreading the three men far apart as they dropped, Jellicoe himself touching down in extremely hilly country some three and a half miles south of the proposed landing place. Fortunately he soon made contact with his radio operator, Sergeant Kesterton, who was himself lucky to escape injury when he crashed down on a steep slope – but there was no sign of the important third member of the party, Major Dolbey, who had been included to act as interpreter and also as adviser in political and Intelligence matters.

What there were signs of, however – and sounds – was agitated hostility all around them, punctuated by more rifle fire, and although danger was not for the moment immediately threatening, it did seem likely that they would sooner or later be discovered by someone, and someone who might be German, not Italian. This placed Jellicoe in a peculiarly difficult position, for he was bearing a personal letter from General Maitland Wilson to Admiral Campioni assuring the Admiral of kindly British feelings and lightly sketching proposals for future co-operation; and deeming unacceptable the dangers consequent upon its falling into German hands, Jellicoe decided that he must follow the example of a host of fictional heroes in such circumstances, and eat it.

Unfortunately the letter-writer had read the wrong books and General Wilson's message to the Admiral was not written on rice paper. It was written on stout official note-paper, probably linen-based, was tough, indigestible and nauseous to the taste, and it took Jellicoe an hour to dispose of it; and as he forced down the last mouthful, he and Kesterton realised that the men whose increasingly noisy movements were bringing them closer every minute were shouting to each other in Italian, and that the exercise had been unnecessary.

Once their identities had been established by the Italians who eventually discovered them, they were hospitably treated. They were taken to an officers' mess and attempts were made to wash away with wine the awful effects of General Wilson's letter, and they were also given some reassurance regarding

the third member of the party. Major Dolbey, whose courage
in agreeing to join the mission was exemplary – for this had
been his first parachute jump, and he was well above the age
when such risks are to be recommended – had been ill-
rewarded. He had landed heavily on the main coast road and
broken his leg, and only his fluent Italian and speed of thought
had saved him from maltreatment when first discovered, for
the Italians had had no notice of the British arrival and had
assumed that the dark forms falling out of the sky were
Germans, for whom they had no liking and of whose motives
they had the strongest suspicions.

Once these misunderstandings had been cleared up,
however, friendship and hospitality ruled, and when
eventually a dilapidated lorry conveyed Jellicoe and Kesterton
to the Governor's Palace, they found Dolbey already there, in
considerable pain but fairly optimistic regarding Campioni's
attitude.

Not surprisingly, this had been doubtful at the start of the
interview with Dolbey. The unfortunate Admiral had learned
of the armistice only thirty-two hours before by telephone
from the wife of one of the German officers on the island (it
must have been an interesting conversation, but sadly it went
unrecorded); this event had been quickly followed by the
arrival of an *Oberstleutnant* from the staff of the commander of
Sturmdivision Rhodos, General Klemann, requesting
enlightenment as to Campioni's reaction to the news and
discussion regarding immediate developments.

During this interview it had been agreed that the Italian
and German troops should for the moment remain where they
were – an arrangement to which Campioni had little option
but to agree, as the Italian troops were chronically short of
transport. Not so the Germans, who used the respite thus
given them to send strong patrols out to the three airfields on
the island (Marizza, Calato, and Cattavia in the extreme
south) in an endeavour to take them over, a move which had
been thwarted around Marizza by the staunchness of the
Italian artillery and was the cause of much bitterness among
Campioni's staff. They all felt that the Admiral should at least
protest at this blatant breaking of the agreement by the
Germans – a suggestion ignored by Campioni, who knew that
without far more military power and efficiency at his

command, there was no point in making what Klemann would know quite well was an empty gesture.

On this gloomy and fatalistic note he had retired to bed, to be awoken a couple of hours later by one of his staff with news of the unexpected British visitors ... and his first reactions to Dolbey's presence and startling proposals had naturally been coloured by his previous mood. But the arrival of Jellicoe cheered him up immensely, for it seemed to him that the British would hardly commit a real English milord to a project they did not intend substantially to underwrite – and so even while he dilated upon the handicaps under which his own forces laboured at present, he became enthusiastic at the prospect of what they could achieve in co-operation with British forces deployed in strength.

The immediate landing of a British armoured division augmented by extra artillery and perhaps preceded by a strong airborne contingent dropped on to Marizza airfield would, he proclaimed, entirely transform the situation. Not only would such a force be welcomed in all Italian-controlled areas, but it could count upon guidance, logistic support and aid behind the lines as it advanced against the German positions, as well as active support certainly from the Italian artillery – and perhaps also from some of the infantry units, if the British brought extra arms for them. The Admiral's staff nodded eagerly at all their chief's main points, and there was a suggestion that even more Italian enthusiasm than he was promising would encourage the British formations as they swarmed ashore – in which regard had they not getter get word immediately to their coastal forces in order to avoid, as dawn broke, a repetition of the unfortunate welcome which had mistakenly been afforded to Jellicoe and his two colleagues? How many hours did they actually have before the assaulting divisions arrived?

This, of course, was the crux of the matter, and although Jellicoe was able to postpone briefly revealing the truth of the situation – and obtain use of the Italian naval wireless station to attempt to pass a few cryptic messages to Cairo – he eventually had to reveal that for at least six days only the members of the mission itself and a few small bodies of Special Service troops would be available. At this the Admiral became glum and rather petulant, but nonetheless he placed a room, beds and the continued services of his doctor at his guests' disposal, and after entreating Jellicoe and his colleagues to don civilian clothing and not to show themselves around the palace more than necessary, he retired once again to bed.

The following day was spent in an atmosphere of equivocation. German staff officers arrived and departed (at one moment Sergeant Kesterton narrowly avoided diving into an air-raid shelter with Klemann's chief of staff) and Jellicoe's attempts to find out exactly what was happening were foiled either by genuine ignorance on the part of most of Campioni's staff, or deflected by Campioni's protestations of sincerity. He was only talking to the Germans, he declared, in order to gain time to deploy his own forces and for British forces to arrive – or at least, this mission about which Milord Jellicoe spoke, which would presumably be able to give him, Campioni, rather more concrete assurances than had so far been produced. The details of the arrival of Colonel Turnbull and the other members of the mission were thereupon agreed, but Jellicoe's attempts to put spine into the Admiral, or even to point out to him that his instructions from Badoglio under the armistice terms demanded strong action by Italian forces against any attempts by the Germans to take over Italian territory, met with faint response.

However, in order to show some willingness to co-operate and also perhaps to expedite reinforcement, Campioni did agree to allow Major Dolbey to be smuggled out of the palace and onto a Cant seaplane which would fly him to Cyprus with a long report from Jellicoe. Shortly after the major had gone, Jellicoe felt that he could indulge in a short rest.

He was awakened just after 1700 by the Admiral himself with the news that the situation had deteriorated rapidly during the afternoon, and that the Germans were about to move in strength into Rhodes town itself. He had, he said, given instructions that Colonel Turnbull should not come to Rhodes for the moment but should take shelter in one of the nearby islands such as Simi or Castelorizzo, and he urged Jellicoe to take himself and Kesterton away as soon as darkness had fallen. As a token of his own good faith, Campioni suggested that his Chief of Staff, Colonel Fanetza, should accompany them, and he would place an Italian motor-torpedo boat at their disposal.

Upon reflection, it seemed to Jellicoe that if Campioni were genuine in his protestations, then his presence there would be an embarrassment without adding to the Admiral's strength, and if he were not genuine, then there was no point in staying anyway. As a result, shortly after nightfall a curious-looking party dressed in civilian clothes which had quite obviously not been tailored for them and carrying a picnic basket and two bottles of Rhodes wine, mysterious packages containing the components of their own wireless set plus maps of the Rhodes defences and of the minefields of the Aegean (which proved in the event to be dangerously inaccurate), left the palace and made their way through the dark alleyways and into the harbour. By 2100 they were on their way to Castelorizzo.

David Sutherland with the men from S and M Detachments who had left Haifa in such a hurry two nights previously were already at the port of Castelrosso on Castelorizzo, having arrived there from Cyprus the previous midnight. There had been some discussion during the passage as to whether hostility or friendship should be expected from the wholly Italian garrison on the island, the first condition necessitating a clandestine landing on the western end of the island followed by a long march; the second allowing instant entry into the port and thus much saving in time and effort.

In view of the fact that many members of the patrols suffered from sea-sickness during the night, it was as well that the second alternative was chosen and proved the more correct. The M.Ls. were challenged from the Italian forts guarding the port entrance, and, perhaps owing to mediocre translation, a few rifle shots were fired at them one of which slightly wounded a naval officer, but eventually one of the attached Intelligence people was sent in by folboat to explain their presence, and shortly before dawn some Italians came out to guide the ships into port. By daybreak the British presence in Castelrosso was secure, and if their reception by the Italians was timid at first, it became more genial during the course of the day when the latter realised that they were to be treated as allies and not as defeated enemies – an impression heightened when honours were paid by the British to the Italian flag when it was run up, reciprocated by a guard of honour on the port office roof when the White Ensign was hoisted.

But if relations between the new allies were friendly, there was still a great deal of deep hostility between old enemies. Castelorizzo, like all the Dodecanese islands, had been handed over to Italy as a result of the peace negotiations following the First World War, and the indigenous Greek inhabitants had lived under an oppressive regime ever since. But although they were kept in conditions of miserable poverty – Jellicoe later reported that he had never seen thinner or more unkempt children – the treatment had not broken their spirit. There had been some surreptitious spitting when the Italian flag had been raised, and later during the day great efforts were made by the enthusiastic and welcoming Greeks to assure every wearer of British khaki that this had been for years the common practice whenever the hated white, green and red colours had been seen – and that the gesture did not and never would apply to the red, white and blue. Later, Milner-Barry was offered a shave by the local Greek barber who apologised for the bluntness of his razor – it was the one he kept for shaving Italians and he had not had time since the morning either to sharpen it properly or to obtain another.

In the meantime Stewart Macbeth and the two M Detachment patrols plus the anti-aircraft crews were sent to the highest point on the island to take over the wireless station and keep an eye on the Italian artillery there and along the coast – where, incidentally, as so often in the Mediterranean campaign, they were impressed by the bearing of the Italian gunners as compared with their infantry. S Detachment was billeted in Castelrosso itself, as were the S.B.S. and R.A.F. signallers, who spent the day listening to and reporting upon a stream of frantic and often contradictory reports of developments on Rhodes.

Dawn the following morning (September 11th) brought Colonel Turnbull by seaplane from Cyprus, and then, shortly after he had carried out a swift analysis of the situation and departed for Simi again by seaplane, the arrival of Jellicoe, Kesterton and Colonel Fanetza, whose entrance into what was to become a convoluted political scene was obviously intended by the immaculateness of his breeches and tunic to be significant, if not actually conclusive. Unfortunately it was

marred by a false step followed by a loud splash into the
waters of the most oily and sewage-strewn corner of the
harbour, and Fanetza's temper at this misadventure was not
improved by the evident strain he saw on the faces of the
British troops trying not to laugh as they helped him from the
water, and certainly not by the hysterical delight of the
Greeks.

To what extent the incident coloured Fanetza's long-term
opinion of his country's new allies will, of course, never be
known, but it was certainly the cause of one almost immediate
contretemps. After a hasty breakfast and an even hastier
conference with Sutherland, Jellicoe set off for Simi in pursuit
of Colonel Turnbull, again accompanied by Fanetza, but the
M.A.S. had hardly cleared Castelorizzo Island when a signal
was received from Campioni ordering them to remain in
harbour.

Jellicoe persuaded the captain, Commandante Del Viso, that the message had almost certainly been sent by the Admiral in ignorance of the fact that Turnbull was at Simi and also convinced him that in any case Turnbull must be warned of developments, so they proceeded on course; but all the recent activity had taken its toll, and, lulled by the warm sunshine and the gentle seas, Jellicoe fell asleep.

I woke up to find that the land which, when I had dozed off, had been to starboard, was now to port and to realise we had about-turned. I remonstrated violently with Col. Fanetza, and the fact that he had given the order purposely while I was asleep and that I had been unable to restrain a smile which he had seen during his earlier and involuntary immersion in Castelrosso harbour, did little to improve our tempers.[1]

There was little that Jellicoe could do about the situation, however, for Castelorizzo was by now close at hand and it was obviously too late for another turn-about and an arrival at Simi before dark – and news awaited him at the port office. Matters on Rhodes had deteriorated even further, and it was now evident that within hours an unconditional surrender to the Germans there could be expected. It seemed that those vital airfields would provide operational bases for the Luftwaffe, not the R.A.F.

But there were other airstrips on other islands in the Dodecanese chain which were not under German domination, and in the opinion of some influential men in Cairo, swift action might still secure them for the Allied cause. On the evening of September 11th, Colonel Turnbull, who had now returned to Castelrosso, received orders to deploy the forces at his disposal in an ever-widening circle. He was assured that the resultant thinning-out would quickly be corrected by the arrival of reinforcements as soon as transport became available, and in token of this, another detachment of R.A.F. troops arrived from Cyprus that same morning.

Turnbull was also soon to receive additional shipping, for at dawn the following day a motley collection of Italian craft arrived from Rhodes (and caused a rapid deployment of S patrols along the quays when somebody realised that the Germans might be perpetrating a 'Trojan Horse' deception), adding to the Castelrosso fleet several small trawlers, two more M.A.S. boats and some large caiques. It still added up, of course, to an extremely exiguous force with which to tackle a complex problem spread geographically over a wide area, but nevertheless that evening M.L. 249 carrying Sutherland and the patrols of S Detachment, and an Italian M.A.S. with Jellicoe, an interpreter and the invaluable Kesterton aboard, set off on the first stage.

13 Sept 43.

Dawn found us off the south coast of Cos after an uneventful night. None of us had had any worthwhile sleep for the last five or six days until coming on board ... but there is nothing so invigorating as sleeping on deck at sea and we were therefore feeling fully restored and capable of appreciating the beauty of the early morning.

Beautiful it was indeed, with the sun just catching the hills of Cos as we rounded the eastern promontory, with the coast of Turkey more mountainous and heavily wooded and very wild, away to starboard. Cos from the south appeared rocky and austere but as more and more coastline appeared trees, vineyards, houses and eventually the town of Cos began to show themselves, the houses glittering in the strengthening sun.

We had been doubtful of our reception and we did not know if the Germans had forestalled us or not, or what the sentiments of the Italian garrison would be. But as we neared the harbour the inevitable crowd of children began to collect and, running through its narrow entrance we saw the crowd gathering to meet us on the quay. The enthusiasm and joy of the inhabitants was touching in its spontaneity.[2]

Grapes were showered upon the patrols as they went ashore, and even some champagne was produced – by the Greeks, of course, for the Italian response to the British arrival was more dubious, perhaps influenced by rumours of recent events on Rhodes. But the garrison commander and his staff were co-operative, and by noon most of the S.B.S. men were occupying billets around Antimachia airfield in the centre of the island, and the officers were sitting down to lunch in the mess, where Milner-Barry and Macbeth were eliciting from the commanding officer of an Italian infantry battalion the defence plan for the area – 'or rather the admission that there was no plan.'

Meanwhile, back in the town of Cos itself, free haircuts and shaves were pressed upon them, and Second-Lieutenant Stefan Casulli, a slight and extraordinary Alexandrian who had joined the British Army and volunteered for special service, was borne shoulder-high to the square and entreated to make a speech.

Jellicoe and his small party, however, had already left, his next mission being to discover the attitude and intentions of the Governor of the island of Leros, Admiral Mascherpa, and if these proved amicable, to investigate the defences of the island and to find a suitable area into which to drop supplies and reinforcements.

The twenty-mile voyage provided its own brand of excitement. A rapidly freshening breeze raised so choppy a sea that the Italian skipper became increasingly agitated, punctuating the trip with expressions of *'C'est grave!'* culminating in a final *'C'est pire!'* – and much later revealing that had it not been for the special circumstances he would never have dreamed of remaining at sea in such conditions but instead would have turned back very early in the voyage.

Fortunately for the party's peace of mind, they had not known until then of the comparative unseaworthiness of these craft, but it was nevertheless with a sense of relief that they slid under the lee of Leros and were soon landing in front of the Governor's Palace, where Jellicoe found the Admiral in a most friendly and co-operative frame of mind. Not so satisfactory, however, was the presence of Colonel Fanetza at the Admiral's elbow, though it seemed that the colonel had not as yet been able to exercise any particularly malignant influence upon his superior.

Food and refreshment were provided, military dispositions discussed, signals sent off to Cairo and to Turnbull in Castelrosso, and then Jellicoe, accompanied by the Admiral, set off for a tour of the island. The results were satisfactory, and later that afternoon a seaplane was placed at Jellicoe's convenience to fly him back to Castelrosso, where he reported in person to Turnbull and then slept soundly for fourteen hours.

While Jellicoe was conferring with Mascherpa and catching up on sleep, Sutherland and Milner-Barry had set about increasing both the strength and area of Allied presence in the eastern Aegean.

Their energies around Antimachia airfield on September 12th and 13th, combined with unexpectedly rapid reaction from Cyprus and Cairo, resulted in the arrival of a Dakota attended by a flight of South African Spitfires during the afternoon of the 13th, followed just before midnight by the dropping of a company of the 11th Parachute Battalion on to the salt pans along the northern coast near Marmari, guided down by a party under Stewart Macbeth. Moreover, officialdom had given the increasingly mixed force operating in the Aegean (for the navy was obviously to become heavily involved) an identity and at least a number – Force 292 – and Cairo now announced that a general had been appointed to command it, who would shortly arrive on Cos. It was time for irregular groups to move on.

Their first brief stop was on the neighbouring island of Kalymnos, where the local inhabitants promptly declared a holiday and the patrols were billeted in a sponge warehouse, for the island had long been the centre of the Dodecanese sponge fishing fleet. The factory and indeed most of the island was owned by a lady of great distinction, inevitably dubbed 'The Sponge Queen', who entertained Sutherland, Milner-Barry and Stefan Casulli to dinner with great formality, and was so enchanted with them that she led them into the garden where she issued them with spades with which to dig up bottles of the most delicious wine, concealed by her for years from the Italians.

The Italian presence on the island was small and pleasant at least to the British, so after making a few suggestions regarding defence positions should the Germans attempt an invasion, Sutherland and the others left with some regrets, Milner-Barry going directly to Samos, a much larger island to the north separated from the Turkish mainland by a narrow channel. Here he established himself at Karlovossi, where, owing to the presence of about 1,500 members of a Blackshirt formation, he found his reception 'to put it mildly, a bit frigid.'

Nevertheless, 'I found life there most agreeable especially after I had established my authority, though only a captain, over the Italians, whether they were Colonellos or not. I found it necessary to chuck my weight about a good bit, and instructed the Italian officers that saluting was essential, as I had been appointed Governor *pro tem.*'

There is no doubt that cheek plays a large part in the success of certain operations, but Milner-Barry was not to remain in his exalted position for long. He and his patrol were sent upon an abortive operation against a non-existent post on Chios to the north, and when they returned to Samos it was to find that a battalion of the Royal West Kents had arrived and that a brigadier, no less, was now in command. It was with little sense of regret that the following day Milner-Barry received orders to return to the delights of the Sponge Queen's hospitality on Kalymnos, where David Sutherland had already arrived. There had been developments to the south which seemed to hold promise of adventure and exploitation.

It will be remembered that when David Sutherland and Walter Milner-Barry had left Haifa for Cyprus and Castelrosso, Ian Lapraik had been left behind at Athlit to collect together all the other deployed elements of S.B.S. – mostly of M Detachment – and bring them up in support as quickly as possible. He had left Haifa on September 12th with some fifty men, including a large number of Royal Marines whom he had seduced from their corps into the S.B.S., and after calls at both Castelrosso and Cos, had been directed southwards again to Simi, arriving there after nightfall on the evening of September 17th.

Despite the fact that Colonel Turnbull himself had been there only a week before and been hospitably received, Lapraik felt that the arrival of strange shipping at such an hour might provoke at least suspicion if not hostility, so he sent in a folboat carrying Lassen and his usual No. 2, Corporal O'Reilly, to make contact with the Italian authorities. It was as well that he did so, for Lassen was greeted with fire from two 20mm. machine-guns, a contretemps which he resolved, characteristically, with nothing more than a powerful voice employing multilingual profanity.

Later, Lapraik himself went ashore to be received officially by both military and civilian leaders, and such was his power of persuasion and debate (he was a lawyer by training) that within a few hours he had virtually taken over governorship of the island. The senior Italian officer was a naval lieutenant, Andrea Occhipinti, who had at his command 140 mixed soldiers and sailors and nine 8mm. and two 20mm. machine-guns, and had Lapraik not taken strong measures, he might have needed them to protect himself and his men from the vengeance of the local Greeks, who hated them all very much.

'I let them know,' reported Lapraik 'that wrongs would be righted in due course, that there would be equity for all, but that, for the moment, the efficient progress of the war rose above other considerations.'

In pursuit of this latter course, he inspected the Italian defence positions and indicated where they should be improved, deployed his own men to the same end, and in pursuance of instructions from Jellicoe to find out what was happening on Rhodes, sent Stud Stellin in through a narrow gap in the minefields on a reconnaissance. He also sent Lassen and three men to investigate Calchi, the small island lying off the western coastline, and to carry out what measures they thought necessary – an assignment carried out with extraordinary relish.

Finding that the garrison consisted of but twelve *carabiniere*, Lassen put them through an assault course, forced them to build machine-gun emplacements and barbed-wire barricades, supplied them with weapons and ammunition and brief instructions on how to use them best, and so impressed them with his orders to defend the island to the very best of their ability or face his wrath, that when a German force did land a few days later, the *carabiniere* inflicted losses and suffered casualties which no mere police force could have been expected to undergo in such circumstances.

Stellin in the meantime had been extremely lucky to avoid capture, for the Germans on Rhodes were well aware of both the strategic value of the island and of the techniques of infiltration and attack employed by their nearest enemies. The presence of Stellin and his companion became known to them, the area of their activities was thoroughly searched, and for five days the pair were harried from hilltop to hilltop until they managed to slip down to the coast one night and thus back to Simi. Their reports left no doubt in anyone's mind that Rhodes was adequately defended and that it would need more than a single patrol to inflict much damage there.

Nonetheless, Rhodes was obviously the strategic centre of the area and thus the most worthwhile target – one to hit as soon as possible, causing the maximum damage before the new commander could erect impregnable defences. It thus merited the greatest possible concentration of force against it, so if Sutherland's detachment at Kalymnos and Lapraik's at Simi joined forces, a significant blow might be struck.

Moreover, there was now another highly experienced raiding force in the area. The Long Range Desert Group had been the first of the 'Private Armies' formed for operations behind enemy lines in North Africa and had a valid claim to be the most successful, but after the surrender of the Axis forces at Cape Bon in May it was quite evident that they had to learn new techniques if they were to justify their continued existence. They had passed the summer and early autumn months in the Lebanon training at the Mountain Warfare School, and they had been an obvious choice for employment in the Aegean as soon as the nature of the campaign there had become apparent.

The commander of the L.R.D.G. was Lieutenant-Colonel Guy Prendergast, and in mid-September he had sent B Squadron under David Lloyd-Owen first to Castelrosso and then on to Leros, then he himself took A Squadron to Kalymnos; and it was about this time that it was realised that Kalymnos would make an ideal base for all raiding forces in the area. L.R.D.G. patrols had been sent out within the first few days, two deep into the Cyclades, one to Stampalia and a patrol of Rhodesians down to join Lapraik on Simi, and on October 2nd, Prendergast, Sutherland and Milner-Barry crossed over to Leros for a conference with Turnbull, who had by now established himself in Port Laki, in order to discuss future operations.

There had been little disagreement on priorities. David Sutherland's diary reads:

> The next commitment was to be a recce in Rhodes with a view to introducing one detachment SBS and approximately the same number of LRDG, to co-operate with a major assault force landing in the Lardo-Iannadi area. This was to be undertaken by

two patrols S detachment under my command operating from
Simi. We were to be prepared to leave on October 5th.

The future looked bright – too bright for us to take seriously the
warning that an enemy convoy had been observed sailing SE from
Naxos. 'Bound for Rhodes' was the universal opinion. Returned
to Kalymnos in an Italian speed-boat with Major Jellicoe, Lt-
Cdr. Ramseyer and Capt. Milner-Barry, and after a frugal fish
supper in a Greek restaurant, we went to sleep full of plans for the
future.[3]

But they had neglected to take into account some of the
wider issues of policy in the eastern Mediterranean and the
Balkans.

There is little doubt that the announcement of the Italian
armistice had surprised the German Balkan Command in
Salonika just as much as it had the British G.H.Q. in Cairo,
and if the latter did have a few extra hours' notice, the former
had the enormous advantage of a system of efficient
military formations already deployed throughout the Aegean.
Moreover, the commanders of those formations had not long
to wait for clear directions, for Hitler, faced with a threat to an
area which provided him not only with bauxite, copper and
chrome but also protection from Allied bomber attack on the
Ploesti oil-fields, hardly hesitated for a moment. The whole
Aegean area and especially the Dodecanese would be held, he
proclaimed, either by a continuation of co-operation between
the Italian and German troops in the area, or, if the Italians
showed signs of obeying the orders of the renegade Badoglio
government, then by German forces alone, who would not
hesitate to use force to take and exert command. Within
hours, German officers were interviewing their nearest Italian
counterparts in the islands and requesting specific assurances
of loyalty from them.

It is impossible not to feel some sympathy for the Italian
garrison commanders. Most of them were middle-aged or
even elderly senior officers whose service careers had been
rewarded during recent years by appointments to these
pleasant and sometimes delicious islands, where danger had
been minimal, supplies from the homeland regular and of
good quality, and duties easy enough hardly to disturb the

even tenor of what resembled a happy retirement.

Suddenly they were faced with real danger and the necessity to make hard choices. Many of them, given the chance, would have been only too ready to welcome the British for whom they felt regard and indeed some affection, in place of the Germans for whom they felt only respect tinged with fear – but few of them knew for certain the attitudes of their subordinates (Samos was not the only island which held a contingent of Blackshirts), and for many of them there were even more urgent reasons to temporise. The British and American armies might be ashore on the foot of Italy, but their own wives and families lived far away up in the north in such places as Bologna or Milan – and how long would the Allies take to get there?

Even more urgently, how long would it take the Allies – in this case the British alone – to arrive here in these islands in sufficient strength to beat off not only the German forces already present with their abundant transport, excellent weapons and efficient organisation, but also the reinforcements which would undoubtedly arrive from Greece should German control of the area appear in doubt? Admiral Campioni's actions might in the eyes of history appear equivocal and pusillanimous compared with those of some of his compatriots, say in Cos or Leros, but how great a distance separated them, when the choice had to be made, from the nearest German military formation?

This was the main consideration which affected control of the Aegean immediately following the Italian armistice. Those islands which previously had held only an Italian garrison – Cos, Leros, Samos, Simi, Stampalia, Icaria – fell easily under the British influence once they had been visited by men of the quality of Lassen or Lapraik; Lemnos and Mytilene to the north, Chios, Kasos, Kythira, the northern Sporades, the Cyclades except Icara and, most significantly, Crete and Rhodes remained firmly in the Axis camp under German control. And once the situation stabilised and the battle-lines could be drawn, Admiral Fricke in Athens and General Klemann on Rhodes could see quite clearly that they held the strongest cards and that if they played them well they could win the whole pack.

The first essential for them was to secure control of the air

above the Aegean by occupying every island which contained
a practicable airstrip. Extra Me.109 fighters and Ju.87 dive-
bombers had quickly been flown into Marizza and Calato,
and on September 17th the Jus. had begun a programme of
attack on the nearest of the airstrips, Antimachia on Cos. Cos
by this time had already received substantial Allied
reinforcement – more South African Spitfires, more ground
crew, a large contingent of the R.A.F. Regiment, and a
battalion of the Durham Light Infantry as main garrison
troops. These last had spent months in Malta and thus knew
all about shelter from air-raids, and if their spirits were
somewhat cast down by so rapid a reappearance of the sights
and sounds of siege warfare, they nevertheless set about
propping up damaged buildings with dour goodwill and
efficiency, and helping the R.A.F. ground staff to fill in
craters.

Their presence had also allowed the withdrawal of the
paratroop company to Cyprus, and of the S.B.S., some of
whom had gone back to Castelorizzo, while the bulk had gone
to Kalymnos in preparation for a series of raids against
German-held islands, especially, as has been mentioned, the
one against Rhodes.

But that enemy convoy mentioned in David Sutherland's
diary for October 2nd had not, as he and his companions had
thought, been 'Bound for Rhodes' at all. It had been bound
for Cos, and it constituted the transport for *Kampfgruppe
Mueller* which, by 0500 on the morning of October 3rd, had
put a battalion of the 65th Panzer Grenadier Regiment ashore
to drive across the neck of the island and meet the 16th Panzer
Grenadiers, who had been landed near Cape Foca. Then
German *Fallschirmjäger* from the Brandenburg Regiment
dropped around Antimachia, heavy Stuka attacks blew apart
the defence posts, Me.109s. shot up the Spitfires while they
were still on the ground or taking off – and chased away the
Beaufighters which came across from Cyprus in an effort to
bring succour to the hard-pressed defenders.

These by the evening had almost all been overwhelmed by
Kampfgruppe Mueller in a series of brilliant but violent actions,
and by midnight the Germans controlled all of Cos except the
dock area, upon which they focused searchlights and sniped
and bombed everything that moved. Small parties of British

and Italian soldiers sneaked their way out of town to climb the hills and make for a rendezvous at Cardamena with the admirable intention of carrying out their last orders, which were to try to continue the fight in guerilla fashion – but most of them were to be rounded up after a very short time.

Meanwhile, all day long Sutherland, Milner-Barry and the men of the S.B.S. on Kalymnos had been horrified spectators of the battle, watching its inexorable progress: the silencing of one defensive position after another, the continuous arrival by sea of German reinforcements, and the unending flights of Luftwaffe aircraft overhead, both virtually uninterrupted. During the morning they had prepared themselves and their weapons to undertake some form of interference in the onslaught taking place only a mile away across the water, but by the time orders arrived for them to land and aid the defenders of Antimachia it was quite obvious that they were already too late; and against the heavy weapons of the Panzer Grenadiers the small arms of a raiding force would in any case have been inadequate.

When the more violent sounds of battle died down and only the occasional crack of rifle shot pierced the night, Milner-Barry and his patrol put to sea aboard a caique of the Levant Schooner Flotilla. They crept around the eastern end of Cos and went ashore on the south coast in a small bay where they immediately ran into a party of R.A.F. men from Antimachia, who told them in detail of the events of the day. After sending the R.A.F. men away in the caique and arranging for its return on the night of 7th/8th, Milner-Barry and his men found a small wadi a little way inland and took up residence there, the rest of that night and the early hours of the morning being spent bringing up from the beach the rest of their own gear, the wireless set and its infernal batteries.

During the following day watch was kept from a high point at the end of the wadi and a dozen assorted army and R.A.F. men were found and brought in, but during the afternoon Private Watler vanished and search parties failed to find him. Then at dusk German infantry were seen approaching in line, driving Italian troops in front, and soon the wadi was full of 'hysterical Italians who attached themselves to us, and the Germans began to mortar the wadi at both ends.'

In desperation, Milner-Barry moved away with his own

men, all the British he had collected and about fifty Italians whom he could not shake off, and a short distance along the coast he found some rafts, built apparently by either British or Italians but then abandoned. As there was no hope of a ship coming in that night to take anyone off, Milner-Barry and a dozen of the more stout-hearted boarded the rafts and for three hours paddled eastwards along the coast in the direction of Turkey; but in time the rafts became waterlogged and they had to abandon their equipment and swim for the shore.

They spent the next three days making contact with the men who had prudently elected to remain behind and collecting more refugees from Cos and Antimachia – a process made more difficult than it might have been by the fact that after the débâcle aboard the rafts, the party had only three pairs of boots between them. However, Lieutenant McLeod's caique duly arrived on time, made two trips to the Turkish mainland and deposited most of the S.B.S. men (who joined one of their own patrols busily setting up a clandestine raiding base in one of the bays in that deeply indented coast) and the bulk of the refugees.

But there were still British soldiers and airmen at liberty on Cos, and on the night of October 8th/9th Milner-Barry, accompanied by Lance-Corporal Watson and Gunner Geddes, returned to the island in McLeod's caique. They immediately found and sent off another batch of eighteen men who had gathered in the bay, and then began looking for yet more stragglers – a gratuitously generous action which proved very fortunate for Lieutenant-Colonel Browne and nearly forty other officers and sappers of his unit, all of whom, plus a Greek peasant whose bravery and help during this time would have placed his life in jeopardy if ever he was caught, were brought out on the night of October 12th/13th.

Altogether, McLeod's crew and Milner-Barry's patrol rescued sixteen British officers and seventy-four N.C.Os. and men, together with a very large number of Italians and a few brave Greeks. It had been a nerve-racking operation, and at the end of it Milner-Barry was flown back to Alexandria to go into hospital suffering from exhaustion and a bad case of 'desert sores', while the rest of his patrol went to Castelrosso – for Kalymnos and the 'Sponge Queen' had been reluctantly abandoned to the Germans.

So had Private Watler – though this was not a decision which he, as a man who had already wandered about behind enemy lines in the desert for eighty days, had been prepared to accept.

Watler had been seen by two Germans during his period of guard duty at the head of the wadi, and realising that to open fire on them would attract unwelcome attention while to return towards safety would betray the position of the rest of the patrol, he had moved away further inland. He had quickly succeeded in shaking off his pursuers but was then captured when approaching the only water-supply, and two days later he found himself with about 1,000 other British prisoners in Cos Castle, about to be shipped off to Greece – a fate he avoided by feigning the symptoms of malaria. A week later he was out of hospital and back in the castle, which now held only some forty prisoners among whom was a signals corporal who helped him obtain a long length of electric flex, down which they both slid the following night.

They were only at liberty for five hours, but six days later they were out again – down the same length of flex, which the Germans had unaccountably failed to find – to creep through the darkness down to the sea and swim out some 200 yards. They then turned and made their way along the coast until they were beyond the outskirts of the town, whereupon they returned to land and climbed to a small Greek village where they were well looked after. From there they made short forays in search of other strays like themselves, and on one such search they found a dump containing 100-octane petrol in forty-gallon drums, one of which they pierced with nails, though in view of the uncertainty of their own future, they refrained from setting alight the resultant puddle.

They then heard that British small craft were stealing nightly into a nearby bay to find people such as themselves, and, their luck improving, they were picked up and Watler soon found himself back at Castelrosso, where, having reported the position of the petrol dump, he promptly volunteered to go back and help destroy it. But three weeks later when he and his patrol went ashore to search the area, the petrol had gone – and much else besides, for the Germans were preparing for another operation.

Gratified by their success on Cos, they had turned their

main attention to the next important island still in British hands: Leros, with its naval port and fortress, long proclaimed by the Italians to be the crucial base from which naval command of approches to Salonika and the Dardanelles could be exercised. But first, there was a flank to be cleared – a small matter of a wasps' nest close at hand which might prove a nuisance. The island of Simi must be occupied, the threat it posed eliminated, and a radio station installed there with which to monitor and exercise control over communications in the southern area.

Ian Lapraik had kept himself and his men extremely busy since his arrival on Simi, for, in addition to Lassen's trip to Calchi, he had sent Lieutenant Simpson down to Scarpanto to rescue the crew of a shot-down bomber, absorbed Stellin's first report on conditions on Rhodes and conferred with Sutherland and Jellicoe on future operations against that island. He had also firmly suppressed continued signs of animosity between the Greeks and the Italians, reorganised the distribution of food and clothing throughout the domain upon a more equitable basis, and deployed the forces at his command in new defensive positions above the town and harbour.

On the day that Cos was overrun Lapraik had found himself unaccountably short of information, so he had gone to that beleagured island during the following twenty-four hours and, not particularly liking what he saw, returned in thoughtful mood – to find that he had unexpectedly received reinforcement. A caique bearing forty R.A.F. men to Cos had, unaware of the true situation, called in at Simi, and they were still there when he returned, quickly to find themselves a part of his defence force and in due course the recipients of a broadsheet couched in tones unlike those of the official directives to which they were used – and, to be fair, unlike Lapraik's own normally magisterial style:

For the R.A.F.

As you have recently arrived in the area you are naturally unaware of the military situation in general, and in the island in particular ... Our situation may be compared with that of

Singapore when the Japs were only a short distance away and advancing rapidly *i.e.* owing to our strategic importance there is no doubt whatsoever that we shall be attacked. It is merely a question of whether it is tomorrow, or the next day, or the one after. Let there be no doubt about it, they will come; therefore we must be prepared ... When a guard is called out it will be in seconds not minutes as was the case last night. When ordered to stand to they will be downstairs and in the bushes like bats out of hell ... We are all doing strange jobs at the moment. We weren't trained as island defenders any more than you were, but we have to carry out the task just the same.

When you realise that the next island to this, Cos, has been attacked and almost wound up by the Germans we can understand the gravity of our position, so for God's sake let's get our fingers out and get weaving and we'll show these bastards what we are capable of.[4]

The 'bastards' arrived on the morning of October 7th, landing a party of about 100 Storm Troops plus some Italian Fascist units from a caique which had crept into Pethi Bay under cover of darkness. The caique itself was hit by shells from an old German 20mm. gun which Lassen had serviced and installed in the school building overlooking the bay, but by this time the Germans had advanced along a ridge overlooking the town, and even penetrated into some houses on the outskirts, from which they were sniping at every British movement.

Reports then came in that other German units had come ashore in some of the small bays on the eastern side of the island and that Italian troops there were retreating in the face of accurate machine-gun and rifle fire, coupled with blandishments addressed to them through loudhailers by fellow-countrymen attempting to persuade them to lay down their arms and return to the Fascist fold. Lassen and the Irish patrol were sent to rectify this situation, which they did by putting in a swift and violent attack on one of the German units advancing a little too openly – a demonstration of power which heartened the defenders to such an extent that, aided by Lassen's 'advice and backing', they remained from then on steadfastly in position and fought their attackers to a standstill.

When questioned on the 'advice and backing' which he had, according to his report, offered the Italians on this occasion,

Lassen's reply was simple but terse: 'I stood behind them and told them to stay where they were,' he said. 'Otherwise,' he added succinctly, 'I would shoot them!'

Meanwhile, Stewart Macbeth had been sent to Panormiti in the south of the island to bring up Italians so far uninvolved in the battle and with them to attack the Germans above the town, while Lapraik himself organised a street-clearing operation intended to drive them either into Macbeth's arms or into the sea – but in order to do so he needed good covering positions in which to set up some of his Bren-guns. One man was killed and three others wounded in this stage of the battle, but by 1300 both arms of the attack were reported in position, and Lapraik gave the orders to advance.

The next half hour was a compression of all the sights and sounds of a house-clearing operation: grenade explosions in confined spaces, rifle and pistol shots echoing through narrow streets, the shouts of anger, fear and fury, and above everything the continuous chatter of Bren-guns, augmented by the higher pitch of a captured Breda which one of the R.A.F. armourers had put into working order and which he himself insisted on working, with great gallantry, throughout the battle.

Stuka attacks added their distinctive howl and the thumps of heavier explosion, but then suddenly the close fighting was over and the town was silent. From the ridge above came the sound of small-arms fire, then the realisation that Germans were retreating along its length towards the bay in which they had landed and in which now waited two small caiques and a medium-sized schooner. They were getting out.

The re-embarkation was carried out with Teutonic thoroughness and skill, covering fire holding back the Italians from the ridge and the S.B.S. and R.A.F. men from the town until the wounded and the bulk of the infantry were aboard the schooner. As it moved out towards the entrance to the bay, the caiques closed the shore, the rearguards fired their last furious bursts and ran down the beach – and the German invasion force on Simi had been driven away.

But there was still another act to play. As soon as Lapraik had seen that the Germans were re-embarking, he sent one of his own caiques out from Simi harbour to intercept, and it caught the large schooner as it came around the point of Pethi

Bay. Had the Germans been ready for it, their own available firepower would probably have enabled them to fight off the caique and possibly sink it, but this unexpected threat caused their skipper to veer closer into the coast in order to give his passengers time to organise themselves. And that small alteration of course brought the schooner directly under the Bren-guns sited on the top of School Hill.

It is not known how many men were killed or wounded during those few minutes as the crew of the schooner valiantly brought their craft around to sail it out of range of both the Bren-guns and the small-arms on the caique, but the decks had been packed and they had been raked from above with machine-gun fire. On Simi itself, sixteen dead Germans were eventually buried, thirty of their wounded cared for in the hospital and six were sent off to prison camps – all of whom were probably luckier than the few who escaped into the hills and were later captured by the Greeks and dealt with in a manner which is probably best not described.

Ten of the Italians had been wounded, one S.B.S. man killed and three wounded, and the R.A.F. had come through unscathed – and Simi had not, for the moment, been taken by the Germans.

It was, however, obvious to everyone that Klemann would not accept the repulse of his *Sturmabteilung* as anything but a temporary setback. Indeed, the following dawn saw the beginning of a series of two-hourly dive-bombings of Simi town which resulted in the death of another S.B.S. man during the morning, together with about twenty Greek civilians. Then in the evening, Lapraik's headquarters received a direct hit which had tragic consequences.

When the dust had cleared it was found that two men were trapped beneath the debris: one, Private Bishop, by the foot, and the second, Corporal Greaves, with a weight of debris on his stomach. The trouble was that any attempt to extract one of them intact from the wreckage would have meant that a huge, suspended mass would inevitably crash down on the other, and it fell to Porter Darrell – an American who had joined one of the Quaker ambulance units which had served in the desert and then volunteered to join the S.B.S. – to explain the position to Bishop.

If he agreed to the amputation of his foot, Bishop could be

dragged clear, the suspended wreckage dropped into the area in which he was now lying – and Greaves then extricated; and in order to save his friend's life, Bishop agreed. The operation was carried out at dawn on October 9th in conditions which beggar description. While Darrell crouched alongside the men holding a light, Flight-Lieutenant Ferris, whose medical equipment had been almost completely destroyed in the same attack which had caused the present situation, was held upside-down by his legs above Bishop, working with little else but a pair of scissors and a small wood saw. One is reminded of the conditions in which Nelson died in *Victory*'s cockpit.

The results were not dissimilar, for although Bishop's foot was successfully removed he died from shock and pain shortly after he had been dragged clear ... and Greaves was also found to be dead when eventually the debris was lifted from his body. The episode constitutes one of the very few in the history of Special Forces about which no one has ever ventured even the mildest of wry, half-humorous comments.

Dive-bombing was almost continuous throughout the next day, and in the evening Lapraik received orders to pull out and begin preparation of a base from which further raiding operations could be carried out; after a slight hesitation, the withdrawal took place on October 12th. All military stores were destroyed if they could not be transported, and the wounded, the prisoners and the R.A.F. men were taken first to Castelorizzo and then on to Palestine. The S.B.S. left last, also for Castelorizzo, where they awaited further instructions – and while they waited, Lassen and Shaun O'Reilly, who bored easily, went back to Simi to find out what the Germans had been up to.

They had not yet attempted another landing, for the moment content with the knowledge that Lapraik and his men were no longer there.

While the battle for Simi had been taking place, cables were flying between Cairo and London with regard to the situation in the Aegean which make curious reading in the light of later events.

It had been quite evident from the days of Jellicoe's first

attempt to influence Admiral Campioni that the key to the situation in the islands would be air supremacy, and that the R.A.F. in the Middle East lacked both the type and the numbers of aircraft to secure it. But at the other end of the Mediterranean were grouped long- and medium-range bombers and fighters in profusion, and the release of only a tiny fraction of them for a short period would have turned the balance quite sharply in the British favour. This had been demonstrated at the end of September, when, following urgent representations from Mr. Churchill, General Eisenhower released six squadrons of Lightnings for action over the Aegean and their presence cleared the Luftwaffe from the skies and seriously worried *Generalleutnant* Mueller, who had been about to set out for Cos.

But after five days, angry signals arrived at Eisenhower's H.Q. from Washington and the Lightnings were withdrawn – for the American Chiefs of Staff in general and the 76 year-old Secretary of State for War Mr. Stimson in particular, did not want to see the development of a campaign in the Aegean. They considered it unnecessary, likely to antagonise their important ally in the fight against Hitler, Mr. Stalin, by developing into a campaign in the Balkans – an area which should surely be a part of Russia's circle of post-war influence – and almost certain to draw in more and more Allied military and naval strength, thus postponing the day when the Anglo-American armies would be strong enough to storm ashore on the French Channel coast and drive straight for Berlin.

In Mr. Stimson's personal opinion, the only reasons Britain could possibly have for wishing to fight in the eastern Mediterranean were connected with vague colonial ambitions which every red-blooded American must immediately resist, and that Mr. Churchill wished not only to avoid a cross-Channel invasion in which too much British blood would be spilt but also to redress the failure of the Dardanelles Campaign of 1915 for which Mr. Stimson judged him personally responsible. As Mr. Stimson was a dogmatic old man, there was no way in which his opinion could be changed, even when the evidence against it was presented by American generals actually on the scene – who, when they tried to press Mr. Churchill's argument, found themselves in danger of replacement for being 'pro-Limey'.

Unfortunately for the soldiers, sailors and airmen committed to the Aegean operations, Mr. Stimson's dogmatism was matched in Cairo by General Maitland Wilson's refusal to accept the lessons of the Norwegian Campaign, of Crete, of Malta or of the loss of the *Repulse* and the *Prince of Wales* off the Malayan coast: that command of the air is vital for all military or naval movements, and even more essential for the defence of isolated positions.

Thus, on October 11th, after Cos had fallen, and in reply to questions from Whitehall as to the fate of the British garrisons which had recently been sent up to Leros and Samos, General Wilson replied to the effect that, having sent the forces up there, it would now be very difficult to bring them back; that their retention in the area was not an impossibility, given Turkish aid; and that their continued presence there would be an irritation to the enemy which might cause them to divert and hold forces in the Aegean which might otherwise be sent to France or Russia.

Why he thought 'Turkish aid' should suddenly become available in such form and substance as to protect British troops under threat of destruction is difficult to see; and a superficial knowledge of German military attitudes in general and *Generalleutnant* Mueller's in particular should have told him that neither were likely to put up with 'irritation' for a moment longer than they had to.

The Royal Navy was the first to feel the shock of German reaction. Two destroyers had been lost on the Leros run even before Cos had fallen, and now, with the last British airstrip gone, the losses mounted. Two cruisers were damaged and another destroyer sunk in the Scarpanto Straits on October 9th, and by the end of the month two more cruisers and two more destroyers had been put out of action and another two sunk – one carrying two rifle companies and the headquarter company of a battalion being sent up to garrison Leros.

Many years afterwards, one of the cruiser captains told the author that these losses, sustained in what he called 'the most pointless campaign of the war', brought him and his fellow commanders nearer to mutiny than any other situation during their naval careers, and only the plight of the unfortunate soldiers on Leros took them back into such dangerous areas again. Mere orders from above would not have been enough.

By the end of October, there were three British battalions on Leros: 4th Battalion Royal East Kents, 2nd Battalion the Royal Irish Fusiliers, and the 1st Battalion of the King's Own Royal Regiment – and they were supported by 5,000 Italian garrison troops, of whom only the artillery manning nearly 100 old and poorly emplaced guns were likely to prove reliable. In addition there were some fifty assorted S.B.S. and L.R.D.G. men who had been stationed in the middle of the island with a roving commission to deal with any German paratroops – whose presence, they were assured, was not expected as the island was deemed too rocky and precipitous for their employment.

The L.R.D.G. and S.B.S. men had been on Leros since the fall of Cos and they had had an exhausting and frustrating time. At the beginning they had manned roadblocks, which might sound an undemanding job but was boring at night and dangerous by day, for they had become the main attraction for the Stuka attacks which occurred morning and night with monotonous regularity. Even when the arrival of more garrison troops released them from such mundane duties, they were still regarded as part of a defence force and not, in the main, released for the type of operations for which they had been trained.

Nevertheless, David Sutherland did manage to secure shipping to send Lieutenant Keith Balsillie and some of the men away on a reconnaissance to Patmos and the small neighbouring islands, and in the first week of November during which the Stuka attacks on the island doubled in weight and ferocity, he was instructed to take a patrol on to Cos. On the evening of November 11th he left for Gumushluk on the Turkish coast on the first stage of the journey, taking with him Captain Chevalier and Lieutenant Casulli with the men of Q Patrol. Only when they arrived at Gumushluk did he realise that in the dark the caique in which they were travelling had missed *Kampfgruppe Mueller* and the Leros invasion fleet by less than a mile.

The Germans arrived off their main landing beaches at dawn on November 12th, accompanied, though they did not realise it, by a surprised Keith Balsillie and his men back from Patmos. These slid inconspicuously in to the beach and scurried quickly off to S.B.S. H.Q., where they discovered that the patrols under Captain Holt were dispersed in a wadi in the 'waist' of the island, while Major Jellicoe, who was in command of both the S.B.S. and L.R.D.G. patrols, was for the moment at Brigade reserve H.Q.

For the S.B.S. the invasion morning passed quietly, though they could hear the sounds of battle around the village of Clidi on the other side of a ridge. As the noise increased, the S.B.S. checked their weapons again and waited, and at noon precisely, in contradiction to the opinion held at H.Q., the sky to the south of their positions filled with Ju.52s. flying in close formation to disgorge some 600 parachutists about 600 yards away, while Me.109s. dived low and strafed every sign of movement on the ground as the paratroops dropped.

Once the first bursts of fire had been exchanged and the parachutists had gone to ground, S.B.S. and L.R.D.G. men concentrated upon identifying the positions of the supply containers and then keeping the *Fallschirmjäger* from them – a sound tactic which paid large dividends. By dusk there were quite a number of German bodies lying out in the fields but only one S.B.S. fatality – all victims of snipers' bullets – and the paratroops had been driven to the upper slopes of the Rachi Ridge between Alinda and Gurna Bays; and when the darkness had thickened sufficiently, it was the S.B.S. who found and systematically looted the excellently packed German containers.

At dawn on November 13th another large formation of Ju.52s. arrived overhead to release yet another 200 *Fallschirmjäger*, but these met with even more misfortune than their comrades of the day before. A minor gale was blowing, and many of those not killed or hurt when they hit the ground were dragged by their canopies across the rocks and low walls while frantically trying to release the harness clips, often with disastrous results. At least two of the transports were hit by anti-aircraft fire as they came in across Gurna Bay and wobbled out of formation over the sea, their cargoes jumping clear, but the majority drowning, the bodies floating for hours beneath canopies spread like water-lilies on the Aegean Sea.

The rest of the day was passed maintaining watch on the German paratroops, but at dusk Jellicoe ordered two patrols out to search the grounds around Navy House and to reconnoitre ground at the head of Partheni Bay at the northern end of the island, where more landings were expected the next day. Another patrol collected rations and ammunition from a reserve cache and in doing so found two deserted jeeps, also laden with stores, which they drove back to the main positions; and all that night, as the previous one, those German paratroops still alive were penned in uncomfortable isolation at the top of Rachi Ridge.

What was not appreciated at the time, however, was that although they might be cold and hungry, they were occupying a dominant position which effectively blocked communications between Fortress H.Q. and the northern half of the island, where the main battles would be fought between a seaborne invasion force being continually reinforced, and garrison troops whose strength would be steadily eroded. Moreover, while the Me.109s. kept the air clear of R.A.F. interference, the Stukas could bomb to destruction every strongpoint which might hold up the German soldiers as soon as its position had been pinpointed.

During that second day of the battle, however, it seemed to the British on Leros that they were holding their own. Their casualties had been heavy but so had those of their opponents – as witness the broken bodies scattered over the central hills and the drowned *Fallschirmjäger* in the bay. There was even during the morning an episode which demonstrated that German mastery of battle was not without lapse, when one of their landing barges loaded with ammunition nosed its way into Alinda Bay under the impression that it was in friendly hands and was promptly blown apart by Bofors guns and an Italian battery.

But the success brought the inevitable riposte by the Stukas, and by noon the Italian battery had been reduced to a smoking ruin, the guns overturned, the concrete smashed, the ammunition scattered and the bodies of the gallant crews left torn and bleeding. By that evening there were only three Bofors guns left in action, these constituting the island's sole anti-aircraft defence.

The pattern for the next two days was a repeat of the first, except that no more paratroops were dropped, thus allowing the S.B.S. and L.R.D.G. rather more sleep and relaxation than they had been lately receiving or the rest of the British on the island had any chance of enjoying. As the hours went by, the unmistakable signs of the *danse macabre* of defeat began to appear in the main battle areas among the British formations. Signals did not get through; patrols sent out on reconnaissance missions failed to return, while those sent on offensive missions were killed almost to a man; companies gathered themselves wearily together to storm a position and found it unoccupied – so they relinquished it, only to be ordered to take it again and find it strongly held.

The battle reached the stage so often seen on the sports field when nothing the losing side attempts goes right, while the winners can take the most adventurous risks and succeed. During the afternoon of November 16th the Fortress commander, Brigadier Tilney, suddenly found himself personally engaged in hand-to-hand fighting around the headquarters cave; seven of his staff were killed, he himself was taken prisoner, and by 1730 the Swastika was flying above the Fortress H.Q. and the island had been formally surrendered.

The men of the S.B.S. were totally unaware of all this. They had spent the last two days in relative peace and quiet, occasionally suppressing the activities of some of the more enterprising *Fallschirmjäger* when they tried to recover their containers, carrying out short reconnaissances down towards Port Laki (one of the most revered L.R.D.G. officers, Jake Easonsmith, was shot by a sniper on one of them), and listening with not a great deal of concern to the sounds of battle away to the north. But on the afternoon of the 16th, Jellicoe decided that he was not in possession of quite as much information regarding the general position as he would have liked, so with a sergeant and two corporals as bodyguards he drove off in one of the requisitioned jeeps to by-pass the enemy positions and try to get through to Fortress H.Q.

He was successful in this, and arrived to find German and English senior officers engaged in agreeing terms of surrender in which he was invited to participate. Realising that it would be as well for him to know as much as possible of what was going on, he remained in the H.Q. for quite a considerable time, and then, having persuaded the Germans that unless he returned to give the orders himself his men would continue to fight, he drove back to his own positions.

Here his news was greeted with astonishment and then with

horror, and his first suggestion, that any man who wished to try to escape could draw seven days rations and Good Luck to him, was regarded with some amazement. There was no question of the men escaping individually, it was agreed; they would all get out together. Less than three-quarters of an hour after he had returned, the jeeps were off with the first load, and by 0315 all the S.B.S. and a number of L.R.D.G. survivors were aboard an Italian caique they had requisitioned in Partheni Bay. During the remaining hours of darkness they made their way across to the neighbouring island of Lisso, and here they hastily camouflaged both the caique and Lieutenant-Commander Ramseyer's M.L. which had accompanied them, then dispersed into the surrounding countryside where each man hid for the day. During the morning most of the native Greeks came out to visit them, bearing food and good wishes and occasionally standing beside the infuriated soldiers and shaking their fists at passing German aircraft – who fortunately did not deign to notice them.

The Greeks later agreed to search the Leros beaches and all neighbouring small islands for other stragglers and help organise their evacuation (most of the Greeks seemed to own their own caiques), and when dusk came, they escorted the S.B.S. back to the beach and cheerfully waved them farewell.

By dawn on the 18th, both caique and M.L. had reached the Turkish coast and anchored in one of the proposed clandestine sites, where they found David Sutherland, Ian Lapraik, Harold Chevalier and Stefan Casulli awaiting them. Three days later after a short rest they were at Castelrosso, and two days later back at Haifa, though Jellicoe himself was *en route* to Cairo – via Samos and Ankara!

They left behind them in the Aegean a scene of undeniable defeat for British aims and arms. Of the four infantry battalions who had fought on Leros during the period of the campaign, less than 250 survivors got away, and when the island was later occupied, the cemeteries, both German and British, revealed a story of fighting of a Thermopylaean intensity.

By the evening of November 18th the last shots had been exchanged on Leros, and during the following two nights, Samos – obviously indefensible once Leros had gone – was evacuated. The staffs, the British and Greek forces, the Italian commander and the Metropolitan archbishop left in a fleet of caiques and landed in Turkey dressed in somewhat outré civilian garb. When a few days later it was discovered that the Germans had still not yet invaded Samos, the Levant Schooner Flotilla, with quite a few S.B.S. men voluntarily aiding the crews, took in a second caique fleet and in two nights brought out nearly 5,000 soldiers and civilians.

So ended the first, disastrous phase of the Aegean campaign. Misplaced confidence in allies, pig-headed obstinacy, and a failure to learn from recent events – all in high places – had combined to send too many brave men to their deaths or to captivity. So far as the S.B.S. were concerned, although they had acquitted themselves creditably, it had been a period of frustration. They were trained for offensive, raiding operations, but since the night their commanding officer had been dropped into Rhodes they had been by turns garrison troops, sentries, and a sort of waterborne Royal Army Service Corps, expending their energies and expertise ferrying men to and fro between the islands and the Turkish coasts, and losing the lives of some very good men in purely defensive exercises.

For them the end of this phase of the campaign was a relief. Now they could resume their proper role – and the islands which had lately witnessed their discomfiture would now provide their targets.

FOUR

The Aegean Island Raids

Ian Lapraik's patrol were the first into action, even while the last of the fighting on Leros in November was still in progress. He and his men had, in fact, been ordered to Leros as reinforcements before the fate of the island had become obvious, and following the collapse there, with everything in readiness for operations of some sort, they sailed northwards seeking for targets of opportunity. And for Lapraik, Simi would always provide those.

Since Lassen's reconnaissance, the Germans had arrived in strength on Simi and garrisoned it to some purpose. A German major and two Italian captains commanded nearly seventy Fascist militia and eighteen German soldiers, in addition to the original *carabiniere*, and they had established strong positions in the governor's house, at Molo and at Panormiti. A patrol led by Lieutenant Bob Bury attacked the governor's house in bright moonlight – not the favourite conditions for such an attack, nor over the best approaches for, as a result of the recent Stuka raids, broken glass littered the narrow pathways leading to the house. Nevertheless, Bury found his way through a large open window on the first floor, located a light machine-gun post on the ground floor and threw in a grenade, then left hurriedly after first depositing a twenty-five pound charge against one wall which in due course effectively blew out the end of the house.

In the meantime Sergeant 'Tanky' Geary, covering the entrance to the house, had watched the gathering of seven

German soldiers unknowingly blocking the escape route to the quay, and, as soon as Bury's grenade exploded and the Germans began to react, he emptied a Schmeisser magazine into the group and then hunted and killed the three who had dived into cover.

Lapraik himself visited another known German billet and threw in a grenade while his two companions dealt with those occupants who promptly ran out through the back door, after which the three moved to the caique yard and set fire to the rope walk, an accumulation of general stores and three small craft moored by the jetty. Nor was this all. Three more of Lapraik's men led by Sergeant Whittle blew up the power station and then engaged Italian machine-gun posts around the small harbour to such effect that all three parties could withdraw in comparative peace and quiet, and an hour before dawn Lapraik and his two caiques were at sea again.

They then made first for Nisiros where Lieutenant Bimrose went ashore to blow up the telegraph station, crater the airstrip, and burn several more caiques under German charter, and while this was happening, more men visited Piscopi to blow up another telegraph station and disarm the *carabiniere*. By the time Lapraik and his men turned south they had used up most of their explosive, but they still possessed ample supplies of ammunition so he took them back to Simi – an island which seems to have held great attraction for him.

On this occasion Lapraik visited an old acquaintance of his, an abbot of the Greek Orthodox Church, who gave him details of German posts not attacked on the previous visit. As a result, another machine-gun post was destroyed by grenades and several more German soldiers killed or wounded, and Lapraik also brought away with him several pro- and anti-Fascist inhabitants of the island – an undertaking fraught with difficulty as the two factions had to be kept physically apart on the quite small craft during the voyage back to base.

The day after the raiders left Simi, fifteen Italian and four German soldiers rowed themselves across the strait to the nearest point of the Turkish mainland, where they gave themselves up. They were to be the first of many.

Lapraik's squadron was now withdrawn to Haifa and its place taken by an almost totally reformed L Squadron. With Langton's return to England, and a series of disasters which had overtaken the patrols sent into Sardinia and southern Italy, it had been necessary to find not only a new commander, but also more junior officers and quite a large number of men. The men had been found as a result of a recruiting drive through the holding depots of the Middle East plus some more seduction of Royal Marines from their Corps, while the junior officers had been selected from the ever-growing waiting list of applicants, bored with their jobs and intrigued by the air of mystery and operational activity which the Special Boat Squadrons were gathering.

One such was David Clark, a young man who combined a vague manner and almost Teutonic blondness with an extraordinary dexterity with both rifle and pistol. He had, until he managed to break free of it, held down what sounds to be one of the most comfortable appointments in the Middle East, and it was always a matter of some puzzlement to his brother officers that however disagreeable circumstances became, he never seemed to regret giving it up. Attached to one of the innumerable clandestine organisations operating in the Balkans, it had been David's task to entertain and accompany high-class agents or such people as officers being dropped as members of missions to guerilla leaders like Tito or General Zervas in Greece, during the days immediately preceding their despatch. It was his responsibility to see that their spirits did not wilt under the strain of waiting, their resolve slacken, or, most important, that the alcohol paid for from his expense account did not cause them to talk too freely in insecure surroundings.

To many it would have seemed the epitome of all their dreams – a long social whirl at government expense, gilded with the glamour of cloak and dagger mystique. But when questioned about it, David responded with his only recorded terse remark: 'Too much bloody cloak,' he said, 'and no dagger!' – and volunteered for Special Service.

The new L Squadron commander was Major Ian Patterson, who had been second-in-command of the 11th Parachute Battalion when their company had dropped on to Cos, guided down by Stewart Macbeth. He had been impressed by what he had seen of the S.B.S. on Cos, but not impressed at all when he later learned that his battalion was to be returned to the U.K., which for him meant rationing, grey clouds and the confines placed upon any military unit stationed too close to Whitehall.

He had met Jellicoe before the war at Kitzbühel, and arranged to do so again at one of the Club bars on Cos. 'I'm rather fond of having my way,' he is reputed to have said during the ensuing conversation. 'You can have it as much as you like,' replied Jellicoe. 'But if I don't like you, you'll go!'[1]

So Patterson arrived at Athlit and commenced the training of the reconstituted L Squadron with a few startlingly Draconian measures. It is a recognised ploy for the new commander of any enterprise to attempt to stamp his mark firmly upon the organisation as quickly as possible, and Patterson found all too many marks for his ruthlessness. First, there were inevitably a few hardened members of S.B.S. whose experience had aged their mental arteries until they believed themselves better than any newcomer and thus indispensable to the squadron; then there were the romantically-minded recruits who had envisaged their future military activity in terms of 'swanning around the ocean', blowing up enemy dumps with loud bangs and spectacular pyrotechnics, and wearing unorthodox and somewhat flamboyant variations of uniform. Most attractive for many of these was the dream of escape from the regulation and discipline of battalion life, together with the resultant freedom from the incessant disfavour of adjutant or regimental sergeant-major.

They had quickly to learn that if such facets of life in the S.B.S. did actually exist, then they had to be earned; and under Patterson the earning took an enormous amount of hard physical work, constant vigilance, and a far higher degree of military expertise than they had ever thought of acquiring. The Royal Marines, almost to a man, passed through the fires of Patterson's training programme without turning a hair, but many from other infantry regiments, and especially from the corps, quickly departed sadder but wiser men. When at the end of his training programme Patterson took his squadron up to Castelrosso, it was as competent as any squadron still lacking operational experience could be, but if he himself was not so violently unpopular as he had been a short while before, he was still regarded by the majority of his subordinates, both officers and men, with deep caution.

As it happened, the first raid to be carried out during

Patterson's tenure of the islands was by Lassen, who had for some time wished to revisit Calchi and allow the *carabiniere* to bask briefly in the sunshine of his approval if investigations on the spot confirmed the stories of their behaviour – assuming, of course, they were still alive and on the island. In any case he wished to see how his defence works had stood up to attack – and had no particular desire to leave the operational area.

He landed on the last day of January, 1944, and found to his disgust that there were only six Italian Fascists on Calchi, and that these had taken refuge in the police station as soon as they heard the approach of Lassen's caique.

'I proceeded to the police station and ordered those inside to open the doors. They refused so I broke the doors open. I took the Italians prisoner, and with them, one typewriter, one shot-gun, six rifles, a wireless receiver, two Biretta machine-carbines and a telephone.'[2]

There was no money in evidence anywhere, but Lassen noticed a safe and was about to blow it – apparently he could never resist experiments, even as a child – when he heard the sounds of a motor-boat approaching the harbour. By the time it bumped softly against the quay, his men were in position, and in the resulting fracas two Germans of the six on board were slightly wounded, but the others were so unprepared for the confrontation and so shocked by its suddenness that they gave up without a fight. Four hours later their craft – 'a launch of respectable tonnage' – was on its way back to the S.B.S. base at Port Deremen, bearing themselves, the Italian prisoners, four live pigs and a most acceptable cargo of general stores.

It also bore a disconsolate and almost tearful Shaun O'Reilly, who, competently wielding his Bren-gun during the brief action, had been unable to jerk the barrel away quickly enough when Lassen, with his habitual indifference to danger or to other men's activities, had crossed his line of sight. One of the bullets had torn through Lassen's boot and left a nasty gash across the top of his foot – and an Irish corporal so shaken that it took several large tots of rum and continual assurance from his officer that it was not his fault, to coax him from the refuge he had taken in the forepeak.

The first raids to be launched by L Squadron men specifically under Patterson's direction were against

Stampalia, under a new South African officer, Lieutenant
Anderson, against Simi under David Clark; and a series
against the outer Dodecanese islands of Archi, Lisso and
Patmos, under Captain Bruce Mitford.

Anderson and his men landed in bad weather after a most
uncomfortable voyage (but such conditions keep enemy heads
down), and the following night sent the bulk of his force under
Corporal Asbery, a short, fair-haired but very pugnacious
Scot, overland towards a small bay, while Anderson himself
and Lance-Corporal Nixon paddled a folboat around the
coast and into the main harbour. The weather frustrated
Anderson and nearly wrecked the folboat, but meanwhile
Asbery and his party cut their way through coils of barbed
wire to lay bombs on a Luftwaffe seaplane at anchor too near
the shore, and were pursued by somewhat erratic fire further
along the beach to a point opposite three caiques of which
two were known to be under German charter where, after
some argument, Asbery and three others reluctantly entered
the very cold water and swam out to the nearest craft. They
placed charges in the engine-rooms of all three (though one
was set not to explode as the caique belonged to a friendly
Greek), and in due course two caiques and the seaplane were
sent to the bottom of the bay – by which time, grumbling
bitterly about their sodden and shivering condition, the
raiders were making their way back to base.

The following night Anderson himself returned to the bay
and placed charges successfully upon two more vessels,
leaving only the one caique afloat in Stampalia. This, needless
to say, was immediately commandeered by the Germans,
thus raising the question of the viability in wartime of kindly
sentiments.

On his first raid – on Simi – David Clark was to be taught a
salutary lesson. Unable even in such critical moments to shed
his casual air, and perhaps unpersuaded of the frailty of a
public school manner as a shield against bullets, he led his
patrol in darkness to the door of a German billet, gently
pushed open the door, stepped inside and addressed the ten
surprised *Soldaten*.

'*Guten Abend, meine Herren ...*' he began, intending to point
out how much more convenient it would be for all if they
raised their hands and came quietly.

But with commendable speed and expertise, their *Unteroffizier* snatched up a Luger, shot out the lights and loosed off another shot at David Clark which would undoubtedly have killed him had it not hit and lodged in the boss of the carbine he was holding across his body. Fortunately for Clark, Sergeant Miller had been standing immediately behind him – watching the performance, it may be said, with some incredulity. He flung two grenades over his officer's shoulder as the light went out and with almost the same movement, grabbed David around the neck and dragged him out through the door. As the grenades exploded, they both threw themselves to the ground while another member of the party raked the doorway from quite close with a Bren-gun until all sounds of movement in the billet ceased. They then made their way back to the shore and returned to base.

There had been ten men in that room, none of whom came out alive, and from then on the Simi garrison rarely moved by day or night in parties of less than six; moreover, there were many subsequent desertions by the Italian troops – so the raid could undoubtedly be counted a success. But David Clark used more orthodox tactics from then on.

Bruce Mitford in the meantime had wrecked the cable stations on both Archi and Lisso, sunk three caiques he had found in the harbour, and captured a large schooner satisfactorily full of German 'officers' comforts', including ten cases of Pilsener lager, thirty kegs of Samos wine and six cases of champagne. This he hastily despatched to base under guard (and was suitably indignant upon his return to find that the supplies of champagne had been seriously eroded), and then called upon the last island in his schedule, Patmos, which he found almost empty of enemy troops but with an indigenous population reduced almost to starvation. Oddly enough, the only authority on the island, the abbot of the monastery of St. John, insisted that any food which Mitford wished to donate must be distributed by a properly accredited member of the Red Cross, and was thoroughly antagonised when Mitford ignored his opinion and set about the task himself – an early example of the kind of troubles with which 'hearts and minds' campaigns are invariably beset.

These S.B.S. raids were, of course, part and parcel of a much
larger campaign, though of this the participants were not all
fully aware. *Operation Overlord* was to take place in five months'
time, and a very great deal of Britain's Mediterranean
strategy was aimed at reducing the strength of the German
forces concentrated in northern France to meet it. On paper it
would seem that the contribution to be made by a force of
barely 100 men to so grand a concept could only be
minuscule, but in the opinion of Middle East Headquarters,
they might, with the aid of the Royal Air Force and the Royal
Navy, achieve unexpected results through a consistent
campaign.

The first stage of this campaign was to entail the
destruction of as much German-controlled shipping as
possible – hence the S.B.S. concentration upon the wrecking
of caiques and harbour installations; hence also the
transmission every night of information regarding German
maritime activity to Cairo for the further attention of the
R.A.F. and the Royal Navy. These measures, it was reckoned,
would produce two results: the S.B.S. attacks themselves
would bring about the strengthening of each island's German
garrison, while the destruction of the shipping would ensure
the retention of those over-strength garrisons on
comparatively unimportant islands.

Once on the islands, in fact, the Germans would be unable
to get off – and as time went by, the S.B.S. net would be cast
even wider until even the far-flung islands in the western
Cyclades or the northern Sporades would be under threat,
and the enemy forced to inject even more troops into ever
more inaccessible defences.

Throughout the first six months of 1944, this campaign was
continued and indeed intensified. On Kalymnos in March,
Anderson took in two patrols, one under David Clark and
another under Lieutenant Dick Harden. Between them they
set alight the main fuel stores and burned a large caique
nearby, but they then found themselves caught in a pitched
battle in the centre of the town in which several Germans and
Italians were killed – a number increased the next day by the
German commandant himself, who followed the quite
common but surely mistaken practice in the German army of
having some of his sentries shot for dereliction of duty.

The next week Patterson himself – in defiance of orders from Jellicoe who considered that the job of a squadron commander was to remain at base and plan operations for his subordinates to carry out – landed on Nisiros, where his patrols captured two German lighters loaded with stores, and in a couple of brisk engagements killed or wounded eighteen Germans and took seventeen prisoners at no cost to themselves. That evening on the way back to base, their M.L. found herself in a running battle with three more German lighters and an armed caique, and when one of them came too close, an S.B.S. signaller accompanied by two sailors leaped aboard as a self-appointed boarding party and wreaked havoc among the tightly packed enemy, some of whom shot each other amid the confusion.

The M.L. having sheered off, Signaller Stephenson and his friends dived overboard and swam to the nearby Turkish coast, later to return to base astride a mule.

At the end of March the periodic changeover was due, and Sutherland's squadron began arriving at Castelrosso from the Lebanon, for the moment commanded by Milner-Barry, as Sutherland himself was in hospital with that bane of military life in the Middle East at that time, jaundice. S Squadron had been making themselves somewhat unpopular at the Mountain Warfare School up in the Cedars and also at Tiberius on the Sea of Galilee, where it would seem that a mixture of boredom and high spirits had produced an explosive mixture, achieving results that took the combined diplomatic gifts of both Milner-Barry and Stewart Macbeth to put right. But if a certain wildness in young men may be a nuisance to the social order, it is an essential for victory in combat – especially the type of combat inherent in raiding operations, which by their very nature produce an atmosphere of piracy and brigandage.

Such an atmosphere attracts unusual people, and among the newcomers who came up now with Milner-Barry was John Lodwick, the fourth of the quartet of highly talented writers (the other three being Dick Livingstone, Eric Newby, and John Verney) to serve with the Mediterranean S.B.S. He was an extraordinary character who had joined the Foreign

Legion on the outbreak of war and had been taken prisoner
with them in France in 1940. Lodwick had been the only
Englishman in a prison camp in France when the Royal Navy
shelled and sank the French squadrons at Mers el Kebir, and
only the loyalty of fellow Legionnaires had saved him from
degradation and probably mutilation at the hands of the other
prisoners, egged on by the amused German guards. Later the
Legion engineered his escape through Spain, and his
subsequent adventures before joining the S.B.S. had included
another brief spell in both France and Spain as an S.O.E.
agent.

Lodwick had come to S.B.S. via the commando training
school at Achnacarry and a spell in Italy, and now from
Castelrosso he set off for a visit to Stampalia to investigate
enemy reactions to Anderson's recent visit. At the outset, he
was most unfortunate, for bad weather twice delayed his
departures and caused a return to base on the third attempt,
and although on the fourth occasion he at least landed with his
men, a piece of sheer ineptitude swamped the dinghy as it left
the M.L. on the last trip in, dropping the W./T. set, some
rations and much of the party's explosives into the sea; and
when at last the M.L. departed, broadcasting apologies
through its loudhailer, it took some of Lodwick's general
stores with it.

Though the episode severely raised the tempers of the
Irishmen who made up the bulk of Lodwick's patrol, it does
not seem to have dampened their aggressiveness. The
following night they took the naval commander of the island
prisoner with his guest that night at dinner, a captain in the
German merchant marine, and then shot up a German billet
and wounded most of its inhabitants. However, attempts to
reach ships in the small harbour were unsuccessful, and the
following night, perhaps slightly conscience-stricken, the
M.L. returned early to take them off after a comparatively
unprofitable operation.

But later in April, Lodwick went to Kalymnos, where he
destroyed the cable station and blew up ten caiques in the
main shipyard, including one excellently equipped craft
belonging to the local Gestapo. At the same time Lodwick sent
Sergeant Henderson and the American, Porter Darrell (who it
seems had now overcome his pacifist principles) to attack a

German billet, and for their pains they were chased over the hills for many miles, laden down with the weight of their Bren-gun and ammunition.

Such aggressive behaviour was now becoming rather unusual for garrison troops in the Aegean. Other men sent by Lodwick to an isolated garrison fired shots at the billet door and even blew up nearby telegraph poles – but the soldiers inside stayed where they were, perhaps feeling humiliated but knowing quite well what their tormentors were hoping for and determined to not give it to them. In their situation, discretion was undoubtedly the better part of valour.

While this was going on, another newcomer, Lieutenant Kingsley Gordon Clarke – inevitably and invariably known as 'Nobby' – had set out to repeat Mitford's tour of Patmos, Lisso and Archi. He found Patmos garrisoned by ten Italians who preferred to surrender before a shot was fired than try conclusions with yet another S.B.S. party, and the other two islands empty of both spoils and enemy.

Shortly afterwards, however, Keith Balsillie on Piscopi had more operational profit to report when he returned to base, lethal though it had been. He had contacted the mayor of the main town with whom he had established friendly relations during a previous visit, who had offered him food and wine – and, apparently, Germans. To Balsillie's query as to the substance behind this last invitation, the mayor suggested that he himself would inform the local German commander of the existence in the town of a fat pig, which might provide food for himself and his men if a proper price could be negotiated. According to the mayor, the German commander, a certain *Leutnant* Urbanitz, would on past form visit the town immediately, intending no doubt to sequester the unfortunate animal or at best demand its surrender in return for paper occupational money – and if Keith Balsillie and his men were hidden along the route, the life of the pig would be saved and Piscopi relieved of an unwanted presence.

However Balsillie might have felt about this invitation to commit what could amount to legalised murder there was no doubt that it was his duty to concur, and the following morning he and his patrol were waiting at the agreed position when *Leutnant* Urbanitz, his quartermaster and two other soldiers, one leading a mule, toiled up towards them along a steep path. When they were a few yards away, Balsillie jumped from behind a rock and called upon them to surrender. Perhaps as a reflex action, Urbanitz reached for his pistol: and Marine Hughes, who having survived so many hairbreadth escapes at one time and another had developed a strong sense of survival, opened fire with his Bren-gun. By the time the magazine was empty, only the mule was still alive.

One greatly relieved member of Balsillie's party was an American war correspondent named Donald Grant. By means of a great deal of cocktail diplomacy in Alexandria, this young man had managed to get himself attached to the S.B.S., and, because he occupied precious space and rations aboard the base schooner, it was adjudged that he might as well 'carry his operational weight' and accompany this patrol. He had, to several people's surprise, proved strong enough to carry his heavy pack over long marches and up steep inclines, but on this, his first taste of action, he had neglected to switch over the safety-catch of his carbine. Mr. Grant was by no means the first to omit this prime essential in his first battle, but he was lucky to do so in company which saved him from the results.

The pace of island attacks now increased. Patrols were despatched as often and as quickly as transport became available for them, generally with specific tasks to carry out on each island – destruction of caiques and harbour facilities or telegraph and power stations; harassing of German garrisons; capture of Italians; reconnaissance for larger raids to be carried out in the future, or simply the gathering of reports on enemy shipping movements or regular air traffic. Always, however, the aim was to make their presence felt, to demonstrate that every harbour, every billet, every manned post was vulnerable to sudden attack.

As soon as Clarke was back from his three-island tour he was sent off to Amorgos, where he found only one German still on the island – in bed with his mistress at the time of discovery. Three men of his patrol were then detached to Nisiros and killed three Germans who discovered their whereabouts and attempted to catch them while they were still asleep in a cave; fortunately Corporal Holmes was a light sleeper and his Bren-gun was beside him.

Only on one raid was S.B.S. the loser – on Calchi, when Captain Blythe with four men and the young commander of a caique, Sub-Lieutenant Tuckey, with his crew were captured as a result of one of the very few betrayals which took place during the S.B.S. presence in the Aegean.

The incident demonstrates two facets of raiding operations which are rarely dwelt upon – the first being that if casualties do occur on such operations, they are rarely slight. The other is even sadder and rather more sinister. After the capture of the patrol and its naval support, Captain Blythe was quickly flown first to Athens and then to a prison camp in Germany, his treatment by his captors the whole time being in accordance with the terms of the Geneva Convention; but it is impossible to say what happened to Tuckey, his crew or the non-commissioned men of Blythe's patrol, for no trace of their fate has ever been found. Perhaps the transport upon which they were travelling was sunk by a British submarine or bombed by the R.A.F.; but it is also possible that they died at the hands of the S.S. or the Gestapo, as did quite a number of Special Service troops before the end of the war.

David Sutherland returned to his squadron from hospital towards the end of April and found himself faced with the possibility of changing the pattern of operations – an opportunity to be grasped in order to retain the initiative and thus exploit the essential element of surprise.

So far, a continuous succession of raids had taken place on islands in the Dodecanese, but few penetrations had been attempted further west into the Cyclades group, an area lately barred to S.B.S. patrols by edict from Cairo H.Q. This prohibition, it was generally thought, was due to the activities of members of the plethora of Intelligence organisations, which, in the opinion of some S.B.S. officers, 'plagued the area'. The need for agents to be properly planted and allowed time to settle in was appreciated, but on occasion it had seemed that too many hands were sticking too many fingers into a very small pie, and for one period, admittedly short, the S.B.S. had been faced with the fact that only one island with a tiny Italian garrison and little else, had been available as a target.

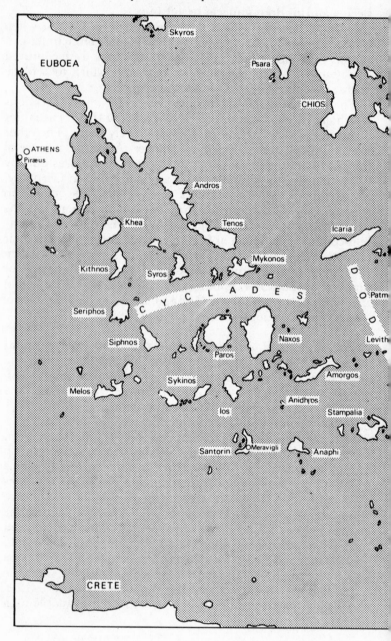

Now at last the ban on operations in the Cyclades had been
lifted, and Sutherland decided to attack several of them, all on
the same night. During the early evenings of April 19th and
20th the tiny fleets moved out of Balisu Bay *en route* for their
objectives: Ios and Amorgos, Mykonos and Santorin.

Nobby Clarke, now a captain, landed on Ios on the evening
of April 25th, quickly to discover that the Germans garrison-
ing the island were occupying dispersed billets and apparently taking little precautions against such operations as he
was about to launch. He therefore decided, somewhat
optimistically, to try to eliminate all opposition in the
preliminary stage and thus be able to carry out his sabotage
missions in peace and quiet. With this in mind, he, Corporal
Pomford and an attached Civil Affairs Officer named
McClelland broke into one of the billets during the late
evening of the following day.

In the first room they surprised two German soldiers in the
act of undressing, who, to the astonishment of Clarke and his
companions, promptly threw themselves at them and attacked
them with their bare hands. No matter how the S.B.S. men
fought them off with gun-butts and fists, they eventually had
to kill both, since time was passing and their nuisance value
was increasing dangerously. But their next capture was much
easier: acting on information supplied by the German's
mistress, they caught him just as he was about to get into bed
with her – although as they marched him along the quay
towards their caique, they were approached by two of his
companions, who, when challenged, opened fire and then
escaped into the hills behind the village.

Corporal Holmes, meanwhile, had been sent to capture
three more Germans in a billet on the far side of town, but had
been foiled when his prey, realising their danger,
snatched up some small children playing in the street outside
and, holding them between themselves and the menace of the
automatics brandished by Holmes and his men, had also
escaped into the hills.

Clarke's preparations for a peaceful day's demolitions were
therefore in shreds, so instead he devoted the rest of the night
to them. Despite the resultant difficulties, both the telegraph
and cable stations were blown up in the early hours of the
morning, together with a fair-sized dump of 75mm. shells.

It was then that Clarke had his burst of inspiration. Requesting the mayor to send messages up into the hills to the effect that unless the Germans who had fled there gave themselves up within the next two hours they would be hunted down and killed without mercy, he and his men sat down to as good a breakfast as their own rations and the hospitality of the island could produce; and within half an hour the five Germans had tamely surrendered and the entire garrison of Ios had been accounted for.

Clarke and his men then sailed for Amorgos where they had a rendezvous with an officer and five men of the Greek Sacred Squadron, whose members had at last resolved some of their political and social problems and also completed a course of training designed to put them into action alongside the S.B.S. Landing on the island on the evening of April 28th, Clarke quickly discovered that the entire garrison consisted of an *Unteroffizier* and nine men, all living in a billet in the main town, and all – as on Ios and the other islands in the Cyclades – apparently unaware of the dangers which now surrounded them.

Seeing no reason for delay, Clarke deployed the forces at his command around the house and opened fire upon the doors and windows with a pair of well sited Bren-guns, while the Greek officer and one of his men lobbed grenades through other windows from the top of a trellis. Then, at the blast from a whistle, all firing stopped and Clarke shouted an invitation to the men inside to surrender – to which they responded with admirable courage but not particularly sound tactics, bursting out through the doors into the darkness with blazing weapons in their hands in a manner reminiscent of some of the melodramatic war films of recent years.

Only two of the ten lived to escape into the hills, and the patrol returned to base a few days later with a score of ten Germans killed and six taken prisoner at no cost to themselves.

John Lodwick had taken K Patrol to what before the war – and even more since – was the tourist attraction of the Aegean, Mykonos. After calling at two smaller islands on the way and surveying them for possible future use, they landed at Lazaretto Bay just before midnight on April 22nd and took up residence in a disused hut above the beach.

The following morning they found that, as on so many

operations in Greek islands, the entire Greek population knew of their presence almost as soon as they arrived; yet there was little need for anxiety, as the Germans would remain in ignorance of it until the moment they were attacked. Lodwick and his men had landed on a Saturday evening, and by ten o'clock the following morning whole families were calling upon them, the men in their tight Sunday clothes with stiff collars, their wives dressed in black and sitting on mules off at some distance, gazing solemnly and throwing flowers to any of Lodwick's men who came within reach.

From the men Lodwick soon obtained the information that, as on Ios and Amorgos, the German garrison consisted only of nine men, seven in a billet in the town of Mykonos, two in the lighthouse at the end of the spit – and 'after considerable discussion owing to the presence of several points of view' a plan of attack was agreed. There is really no point in attempting to better John Lodwick's own report on what followed:

> At 0530 we arrived at the house unobserved, and sheltered beneath the garden wall. The sentry was seen on the balcony and from 40 yards Pct. Lynch shot him through the fifth rib on the right side. The sentry, subsequently identified to be the Unteroffizier I/C died in two minutes.
>
> We then rushed the lower balcony, three grenades, two No. 36 and one phosphorus were thrown up the stairs, and the Germans, who later declared that they had sprung out of bed at the first shot, replied with two more, a small piece from one of which went into my behind.
>
> S.B.S. personnel, who were bunched on the balcony, then scattered and began to fire at all the windows. Orders were shouted to the Germans to come out and surrender but they did not reply. At about this time I threw a phosphorus grenade at a broken window, the aim missed and Cpl. Conby and myself were burned in the face and hands; I should not have attempted this with so many of our own men nearby.
>
> Meanwhile Pct. Perkins had neutralised the W/T room from outside, the aerial had been destroyed and the set was unusable. The attack now developed into a siege and the S.B.S. personnel gradually withdrew from the balcony, taking up positions from which they could fire at the windows though Cpls. D'Arcy and Conby with Pct. Jarrell all entered the house on different occasions, Pct. Jarrell capturing a Schmeisser on the unoccupied first floor.[3]

Obviously other tactics were now needed, for on raiding operations time plays a vital factor. Sending for the mayor who had a German wife and spoke the language well, Lodwick instructed him to tell the men inside the beleaguered house that they stood in no chance of rescue, but at that point a flight of six Ju.88s. flew along the Mykonos Channel, and the Germans, falsely encouraged, fired Very lights, despite the fact that any attempt to stand upright inside their billet brought a stream of bullets through the window from Pct. Hancock's Bren.

Stalemate might have resulted, but then three young Greeks who had volunteered to help arrived, bringing with them one of the two Germans from the lighthouse. They had captured him on the road along the spit, and he was now witness to the activities of some thirty other Greeks, rolling drums of German petrol along the road towards the billet. The intention, he was informed, was to stack it against the house, fire it and burn the entire structure to the ground and anyone who remained inside it to death. It took only a few minutes for him to convince his compatriots of the seriousness of their position.

> No sooner was the surrender concluded than about 500 Greeks invaded the house and stripped it of all its food supplies. We succeeded, however, in collecting all the German papers in the building, and after a light lunch at the local hotel we all returned to Lazaretto Bay by mule. The Greek guerillas were again sent out to collect the second German from the lighthouse. He was found in the middle of the road firing Very lights, and was escorted back to base by Cpl. D'Arcy and Pct. Jarrell from the town.
>
> At 2040 hrs. April 24th we sailed from MYKONOS.[4]

They arrived back at base on the afternoon of April 27th.

Lassen, whose foot wound had turned septic and put him into hospital for a time, had been promoted to captain – and he now took two patrols to Santorin. One was nominally under command of Stefan Casulli and included Sergeant Jack Nicholson, Sergeant B.B. Henderson (whose initials, combined with his mania for sunbathing and physical fitness in general had earned him the derisive soubriquet of 'Brown Body'), Shaun O'Reilly and Corporal Kahane, a fluent German speaker. The other patrol was under command of Keith Balsillie and included the redoubtable and recently promoted Corporal Wally Hughes.

En route for Santorin they called at the tiny island of Anidhros, and Lassen's report tells of 'good anchorages though they are not all weather. There is water, but it is very dirty and only fit for cattle to drink.' They also picked up a slightly wounded flight-sergeant from another island, and then on the night of April 22nd/23rd both patrols were landed on the east coast of Santorin (also called, with that infuriating Greek prodigality with names, Thira), but as there were no good anchorages at all in the area, the H.D.M.L. and the two caiques which had brought them sailed on to another island nearby.

During the following day, information was gathered and plans laid. Three attacks would be mounted, the first by Keith Balsillie and his men who would climb to the highest point of the island and destroy the W./T. station and its outpost near the village of Meravigli; the second would be made by Sergeant Henderson on his own, his task to attack and capture or kill the German commander, *Leutnant* Hesse, and his orderly in the house sequestered for their use. And Lassen himself would lead the rest of the men against the main billet, which was reputed to hold thirty-eight Italians and ten Germans.

'This report was partly false,' Lassen wrote afterwards, with a distinct note of disappointment. 'There were less than 35 men in the billet.' He continued:

> We succeeded in getting the main force into the billet unobserved, in spite of barking dogs and sentries. The living quarters comprised 12 rooms ... it was our intention to take the troops there prisoner. This idea had to be abandoned, and will have to be abandoned in the future, until raiding parties are issued with good torches.[5]

In default of the torches, a systematic but ruthless policy was followed, Sergeant Nicholson kicking open the door of a room, Lassen throwing in two grenades, Nicholson then raking the room – especially the corners – with Bren-gun fire, after which Lassen would go in and finish everything off with his pistol. Incredibly, those two came out unscathed, but Stefan Casulli, following the same practice but standing *in* the doorway instead of to one side of it, received a burst through his chest and died almost instantly, while outside the billet Sergeant Kingston caught a bullet in the stomach.

Marines Trafford and Harris were also slightly wounded outside the billet when a German patrol and some of the sentries opened fire, but at that moment two things happened to distract both danger and attention from them. First, a fear-crazed Italian jumped from an upper window, and as the billet was in fact the office of the local branch of the Bank of Athens he had a forty foot drop to endure; then Sergeant Nicholson emerged from the main doorway and dispersed the enemy with his Bren-gun, firing from the hip.

In the meantime, Keith Balsillie had reached Meravigli in good time but had found the lay-out of the outpost and W./T. station not as expected. The posts were all, in fact, contained in three neighbouring houses, so after stationing Corporal Hughes and Bombardier Fowler in covering positions with their Brens, Balsillie and the others quietly entered the first. In it they found a man asleep in bed, whom Kahane gently awoke.

'For you, my friend, the war is over,' Kahane informed him in German. 'Now be a good fellow, get dressed and take us to your comrades. But first tell us where the wireless set is.'

Undoubtedly impressed by the considerable firepower in the hands of Kahane's associates but unable completely to throw off the bonds of discipline, the man led the party to the next house and almost formally introduced them to his *Unteroffizier*, who himself, convinced by the logic of the Tommy-guns, took them back to the first house where they found not only the W./T. but also three more Germans in bed, apparently too deeply asleep to have heard the previous entry.

The W./T. was prepared for demolition, three more Germans were collected from yet another house, and in due course Balsillie, his corporals and his men together with their eight prisoners made their way back towards their rendezvous with Lassen, which they reached about 0330. As they trotted back down the first slope they were cheered by the sounds of the W./T. installation being blown to pieces.

Sergeant Henderson had not been quite as successful as the others, for not only did the lay-out of his target differ from what had been deducted from the information to hand, but his quarry did not react in the expected fashion. Working on the assumption that at the sounds of battle the German commandant would at least send someone to find out what was happening even if he did not emerge himself, Henderson stationed himself in the shadows of the front garden, by the door.

But when the crash and rattle of Lassen's attack came echoing up towards the house, there was no apparent reaction at all. Puzzled, Henderson threw a grenade which blew out a window and then a second which went through and exploded in the front room, but not until he was actually climbing through the shattered frame did he hear any sounds of occupation – a murmur of voices from the rear which prompted him to drop back into the garden and double smartly around to the back garden gate.

But he was too late – for as he raced around the corner he heard other footsteps in an equal hurry fading rapidly away into the distance, increasing speed remarkably after the explosion of the grenade which the thoroughly frustrated sergeant hurled after them. Lassen was not impressed by Henderson's report half an hour later; in fact, he was not much impressed by several facets of the actions which had taken place, as his 'notes' at the end of his own reports indicate:

> There is no doubt that shooting up barracks at night requires a great deal of skill and experience, such as only the older men in the S.B.S. have, and which will not be found in reinforcements.
>
> Lack of experience must be made up by rigid training, especially in Street and House fighting, and they should be generally taught how to look after themselves; not to stand in front of doors, for example. The standard of marching among the recruits was poor ...
>
> As usual Sgt. NICHOLSON, Cpl. SIBBET and Cpl. O'REILLY did extremely well, and were calm and efficient during the action.[6]

By April 29th, Lassen, his men and his ships were all back at base.

To Sutherland as he listened to the accounts of that epochal forty-eight hours in the Cyclades, two factors seemed evident. Of the thirty-nine men he had sent out, only two had not returned alive and only three had been even slightly wounded, but they had between them killed forty-one enemy soldiers, wounded twenty-seven and brought nineteen back as prisoners – in addition to carrying out destruction of enemy communications and shipping.

Quite obviously, one of the strategic aims of these operations would soon be achieved and many more German troops would be sent out to reinforce the island garrisons. Equally obviously, this would take some little time to arrange, even given the German organisational talent – so if he moved quickly, his squadron might achieve yet more successful lightning strikes while the opposition was still weak. Lassen could go out again almost immediately.

Perhaps German reaction time was a little underestimated; perhaps more thought should have been given to reconnaissance, for when Lassen and his thirteen men arrived on the coast of Paros, they found rows of pitched tents alongside a newly constructed airstrip, and although the occupants were workmen of the Todt construction organisation and not soldiers as such, they nevertheless kept an excellent guard. Wisely, Lassen made no attempt to force penetration through so alert a screen and withdrew – but not before sending out Sergeant Nicholson on one lone mission and Pct. Perkins, another fluent German speaker, on another.

Perkins surprised a German officer who unfortunately refused to accept his assurance that the war was over for him and had to be killed, and although Nicholson persuaded another German officer to accompany him peacefully (the officer was perhaps rendered more tractable by the fact that he was wearing nothing except a flowered dressing-gown), a fight developed as they both left the house which Nicholson resolved with fragmentation grenades, killing his attackers but unfortunately also killing his prisoner in the process – much to Nicholson's disquiet, as the man had appeared friendly and well disposed.

While Lassen was being frustrated at Paros, Nobby Clarke

and Sutherland were preparing for more far-flung operations, and on May 16th Clarke and another newcomer to S.B.S., Captain Stobie, landed on Naxos with two patrols to make contact with a reputed guerilla unit there. In this they were successful, so, despite the fact that the German garrison was not only alert as a result of the Paros raid but excellently dug-in around the most worthwhile target, Clarke decided to combine with the guerillas and attack a small German billet in the town of Naxos itself, reputed to hold an officer and seventeen German soldiers.

The result was a pitched battle in which time was on the side of the defenders, but in the hour which was all Clarke would allow himself one of the two houses of which the billet consisted was completely demolished by plastic bombs, and a considerable weight of fire was poured into the second, from which, however, a strong resistance continued up to the moment Clarke gave the signal to withdraw. But he and his men were left undisturbed by the enemy for the next three days until transport arrived to take them home, with three men slightly wounded and one very weak from malaria.

This was the last main strike by Sutherland's squadron, though Sutherland himself paid a visit to the lovely island of Siphnos capturing a caique and one German soldier in the harbour, and Harold Chevalier ranged the waters to the north of Samos with a mixed fleet engaged upon pure piracy. Small craft he looted of anything obviously belonging to the enemy and then despatched them on their way with warnings of ever-increasing danger to German-chartered shipping; one large caique with its German crew he captured entire and brought it and its cargo of general stores, plus crew, back to base.

After the climax of the raids of April 22nd, perhaps these operations were less spectacular and less obviously worthwhile; but there were still the 'invisible' profits of effect upon enemy morale and, more importantly, upon enemy dispositions. By early May nearly 4,000 extra German troops had either arrived in the Aegean islands during the previous few weeks or were on their way there, and this was in addition to the six admittedly tired and under-strength divisions resting from their ordeals on the Russian front, who had been there at the beginning of the period.

Thus when Ian Lapraik's M Squadron came up into the

area to take over, it was inheriting a situation ripe with danger. Every island within easy striking distance of the Gulf of Cos had been visited twice or even three times, while the garrisons of those further out, if they had not been attacked themselves, had heard disturbing reports of what had happened to their neighbours. No longer did a German posting to the Aegean islands promise comfortable nights in barrack beds or village cottages; they were spent instead in heavily-wired trenches or machine-gun posts, or on watchful patrols of at least three men under the stern eyes of demanding N.C.Os.

But if the days of retsina and pomegranates were over for the defenders, those of hit-and-run raids and easy triumph were also over for the attackers. As Andy Lassen somewhat obliquely remarked, 'You can do some of it, part of the time, for quite a while. But you can't do all of it all the time for very long.'

Stewart Macbeth brought up the first part of M Squadron, and it was soon obvious what Lapraik's orders to him had been. Within a few days, small parties of S.B.S. were aboard naval M.Ls. departing for very distant waters, and by mid-June Lieutenant Lees with three men and Lieutenant Bury also with three, were up in the northern Sporades in search of information and potential targets, while Captain Bimrose with a much larger force was *en route* to Kythira off the southern point of the Peloponnese.

They met with mixed fortunes. Jimmy Lees and Bob Bury encountered very little in the way of enemy opposition, but Lees became involved in politics and the local branch of the Greek Communist guerilas, E.A.M., who were later to make so much trouble on the Greek mainland; in the end he had to evacuate half the population of one of the islands in view of possible repercussion if and when the Germans next visited it.

Charles Bimrose and his party, however, ran into considerable trouble as a result of bad weather, which made it impossible for them to land on Kythira, depositing them on the mainland instead. Here they were first arrested by the local guerilas of E.L.A.S. (the military wing of E.A.M.) who refused to believe that they were British, and when at last their identity was established, they found themselves caught up in one of the periodic drives against Partisans carried out by the occupying forces. This undoubtedly gave them experience of operating with local guerillas which was to come in useful later on, but for the moment they had other duties to perform, and it was with some relief that eventually they were picked up on the coast by their naval escort and returned belatedly to base.

Another operation was then mounted against Kalymnos – taken in by Jimmy Lees – but it did little but confirm the picture painted by Sutherland. Enemy garrisons were now strong and alert, and when Macbeth decided further to test the defences by putting in an even larger party containing fifteen men from the Sacred Squadron and ten from the S.B.S., the result was a pitched battle, which, if it could be judged at all a victory for the attackers, was certainly Pyrrhic, for three men had been wounded so badly that they had to be left behind to be taken prisoner.

It seemed that a dangerous point of balance had been reached, and when Lapraik eventually came up to his new base at Yedi Atalla in the Gulf of Cos, he undoubtedly faced a daunting task if he were to restore S.B.S. dominance in the area.

He dealt with it in a typical manner, but one which shed an illuminating light on the departure from the Courtney tradition which had taken place in S.B.S. training and practice during the preceding eighteen months. Lapraik had been trained in the original commando philosophy and technique, and if events had then conspired to divert him into relatively small-scale raiding, he had certainly not forgotten how larger-scale operations should be mounted. Once Macbeth's reports had been studied and their reinforcement of the previous accounts appreciated, Lapraik began, with Brigadier Turnbull's support, to draw up plans for a full-scale commando-type assault which would deploy over 200 men in the target area, destroy the enemy garrison and defence-points, hold them for as long as it would take to wreck all permanent enemy installations, and withdraw when it became apparent that an overwhelming counterstrike force was assembling.

The target area, almost needless to say, was to be the island

Landing Craft Motor (L.C.M.), useful for taking stores in to a static position.

Castelrosso, the port on Castelorizzo, forward base for S.B.S. after September 1943.

Above Walter Milner-Barry
en route to the islands.
Below David Clark.

S.B.S. schooner in Turkish waters.

Simi, July 1944. From right to left, Richard Lea, Kenneth Fox, Ian Lapraik, Brigadier Turnbull, Lieutenant-Commander Ramseyer and Lieutenant-Colonel Travakis (Greek Sacred Squadron).

Evening in the Gulf of Cos.

Base stores being loaded.

Greeks of the Sacred Squadron who remained in the Aegean with
Lapraik when S.B.S. moved to Adriatic waters.

German Landing Craft with anti-aircraft gun, captured by Patterson's squadron.

Ex-members of the post-war S.B.S. at a recent reunion in Southern England.

of Simi, but its geographical situation as an objective for this radical change in S.B.S. practice now revealed a startling deficiency in S.B.S. capability.

The assault force would be at its most vulnerable during the journey to and from the island, for the ten motor-launches and two schooners which would carry them – despite the firepower and expertise of the men aboard – were neither fast enough nor sufficiently heavily armoured to withstand attack by conventional German naval forces such as destroyers. And of these, two were moored alongside quays in the main harbour at Leros, together with some smaller vessels similar to British corvettes.

In the days of Tug Wilson or Ken Allott, such a concentration of enemy shipping would have constituted a far more tempting target than the garrison defences of Simi or indeed any other island, but although Marine (now Sergeant) Hughes was still present, the aggressive use of folboats had been a dying practice in the S.B.S. for a long time now and their use was restricted almost solely to the transport of personnel from main carriers into secluded enemy bays. Apparently, there was no one now on S.B.S. strength with the skill and experience to carry out one of the main tasks for which Roger Courtney and the first men of the Boat Section had trained so assiduously in the waters around Arran: ship attack.

They must therefore find others who had those skills – become, in fact, clients of those who now possessed the specialisations which were once their own. They found them in Sergeant Hughes's original corps, the Royal Marines, hidden under the intentionally vague-sounding title of the Royal Marine Boom Patrol Detachment, whose reputation was already firmly established by their extraordinary success in penetrating seventy miles up the Gironde into the port area of Bordeaux where they then, with admirable precision, put four large enemy merchantmen out of action. Though the episode had not by then attained the general publicity it was later to achieve through book and film, its outline was known among Special Service troops, and when the R.M.B.P.D. sections arrived in the Middle East, their activities were regarded with interest which quickly grew into respect.

During June three pairs of Royal Marine canoeists arrived

at the S.B.S. base at Penzik Bay, one of the deepest and more
sheltered indentations in the Turkish coast not far from
Bodrum, and one moonless night towards the end of the
month they left aboard an H.D.M.L. bound for Leros
harbour. *Shrimp* was the first canoe to go in, gently
manoeuvring over two 'booms' and gliding almost invisibly
towards her target – but not quite invisibly enough, for as she
approached she was seen and challenged from the target's
deck. Corporal Horner, primed for such an eventuality, called
back '*Brandenburger! Patrola! Patrola!*' and, ignoring the rope
thrown to them, he and his partner paddled on past the ship
and into the shadows of a nearby cliff, where they waited to
observe the subsequent activity.

Shark had followed *Shrimp*, and *Salmon* was the last to make
the attempt and the only one to be challenged while crossing
one of the booms. Ignoring the interruption, *Salmon*'s pair
vanished into the darkness of the harbour where during the
next two hours they found not only their main target but also
one of the smaller escort ships, to both of which they attached
limpet mines with long-delay fuses. In the meantime, *Shark*,
with Lieutenant Richards and Marine Stevens aboard, had
also found their main target and placed their limpets, then
moving silently around the moorings until they had found and
similarly decorated two more of the escorts.

By now the three canoes had been inside the harbour for
over two hours, and *Shark* and *Salmon*, having disposed of their
charges, withdrew. *Shark* reached the lying-up area on
neighbouring Kalymnos quite easily, but *Salmon*, which had
developed persistent leaks, did not reach the island until
daylight when its two canoeists were welcomed and sheltered
by a friendly Greek.

In the meantime the limpets had exploded, sinking the
three smaller escorts and so damaging the two destroyers that
the engine-rooms of both were flooded and some crew-
members drowned; but the German garrison and naval
strength had been fully aroused and search parties were quickly
scouring the immediate environs of the harbour, the coastline
and the nearby waterways. As it happened, they failed to find
either the crews on Kalymnos, or even the *Shrimp*, whose crew
had decided to hide on Leros during the following daylight
hours in the hope that an opportunity might arise to place their

charges during the following night. Nevertheless, the search parties had come so close during the late afternoon and evening that Corporal Horner decided that it would be prudent to slip away as soon as daylight began to fade, especially as the limpets of the other two pairs had obviously done their work so

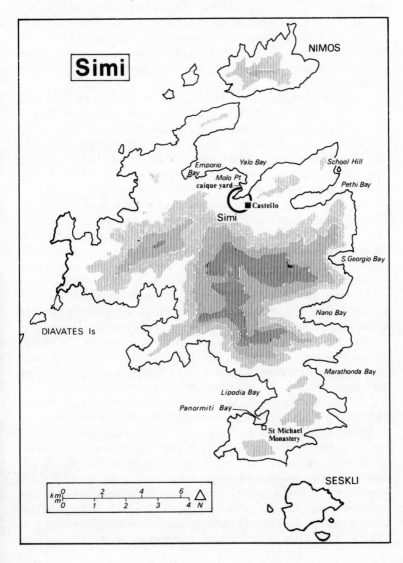

successfully that there were no worthwhile targets left for his
own.

At 2300 that night, all three pairs heard the radio call-sign
from the returning H.D.M.L., all three replied, all were
picked up safely and by dawn were back at the S.B.S. base.
Some days later the German destroyers were laboriously
towed back to Athens with hundreds of tons of sea-water
slopping about in their hulls (they were later sunk by Allied
bombers), and as the *Kriegsmarine* had no replacements
available in the area, the way was now open for the big raid on
Simi.

Lapraik divided his forces, now consisting of his own
squadron and the Greek Sacred Squadron, into three parties
which landed on Simi during the night of July 13th. By dawn
all were overlooking their target areas, the only casualties so
far being two Greek officers who had fallen into the sea during
disembarkation and drowned under the weight of their packs.
South Force under Stewart Macbeth was closed up around
the monastery of St. Michael down in the south of the island,
West Force under Charles Clynes was ashore on the northern
arm of the bay which held the main caique yards, while the
Main Force and Turnbull's headquarters were on the south-
eastern edge of Simi town itself, its immediate target the
medieval Castello which held the German headquarters.

At dawn the attack on the castle opened – for many present
the first such action in which they had taken part despite their
considerable raiding experience, despite also the medal ribbons
many of them wore on more formal occasions. Multiple
machine-guns chattered on each side, searching the
embrasures with covering fire while riflemen worked their way
forward to closer assault positions; mortars thumped behind
them, their bombs crashing on the battlements or disappearing
behind the walls to explode within the castle perimeter itself.

Down in the main harbour, two 'Ems' barges which had
weighed anchor just before dawn came rapidly back, pursued
by five of the motor-launches which had landed the Main
Force on the coast and were now coming in to add their
Oerlikon fire to the assault on the castle. Caught between the
naval fire and the Bren-guns of the West Force already in the
caique yards, the barges quickly hoisted white flags and ran
ashore, but without sufficient momentum to do themselves

damage. In the meantime, Stellin had cleared Molo Point to the north of Simi town and what prisoners he had taken were locked in a church, while more men began to move down towards the caique yards ... but they had to cross a bridge within sight and range of a keen-eyed and expert shot on one of the castle ramparts, and three men found themselves pinned down. It was extremely uncomfortable and as the sun rose, very hot – though as one of them said later, not so hot as when they tried to move.

Meanwhile, South Force under Macbeth had opened their attack on the monastery with a heavy mortar bombardment, following it with a straightforward infantry assault in the face of which the surviving and well outnumbered Germans courageously withdrew to positions on one of the spits jutting from the southern end of the island, from which they maintained a spirited defence. Such was their morale that the first attempt at securing their surrender was rejected haughtily as illegible, but later a young Greek girl went in to them carrying a more formal suggestion for surrender, and by this time it had become obvious to the German officer in command that his thirty-three men were in a hopeless position, so he ordered them to lay down their arms.

But now something of a stalemate had built up in Simi itself. Main Force had managed to work the forward patrols to within 500 yards of the castle walls, but there was no nearer cover, darkness was a very long way off, the resistance from the German garrison showed no sign of weakening, and the ammunition supplies for the attacking mortars and machine-guns were shrinking at an alarming rate.

In view of the undoubted solidity of the castle walls and the spirited defence against which they were pitted, both Turnbull and Lapraik therefore decided that their best hope lay in subterfuge. Orders were sent down to Clynes in the caique yards to cause as many loud explosions as possible and to send some of his men to make a display of force on the far side of the castle, while the Main Force patrols spread out wider and let their expanding presence be seen and felt. An hour later, one of the German petty-officers from one of the Ems barges was sent up to the castle with the suggestion from Brigadier Turnbull that as the garrison was now completely surrounded and the whole of the rest of the island in British hands, further resistance on the German side would be as futile as it would be costly.

It took three hours, the persuasive talents of two German-speaking members of the force – Lieutenant Kenneth Fox and Lieutenant-Commander Ramseyer (the naval liaison officer) – and expenditure of a great deal of ammunition to convince the German commander of the hopelessness of his position. As the arguments raged on and on, the bullets whined and cracked against the castle walls, mortar bombs whooped down to explode with ear-splitting crashes in the courtyard (one narrowly missed Ramseyer and he was deaf in one ear for days afterwards), and from the harbour came muffled thuds as Clynes used up every ounce of explosive he could find while some of his men fished with hand grenades.

But at last the business was over, Fox and Ramseyer appeared waving their hands, the Swastika came down, the German garrison marched out and handed over their arms – and the S.B.S. men pinned down on the bridge could move again.

Ten minutes later, three Luftwaffe planes arrived overhead and bombed S.B.S. positions, then dropped a message inside the castle instructing the commander to hang on as relief was being organised.

'I thought they had forgotten us,' the German commandant remarked sadly. 'I radioed for them five hours ago.'

By this time, the local population had swarmed out to welcome the liberating Allies and also to let them know that the German commandant and garrison had acted during their stay with as much kindness and consideration as had been possible. As a result, once the Germans had been disarmed and had realised that they were not all going to be shot out of hand, a festive mood seized all present, an ox was roasted in the caique yard, the German prisoners even produced wine from various hiding places, and Lapraik having been recognised from his previous visits to the island was called upon to make a speech.

'I admired these islanders intensely,' he wrote later, 'for they well knew that we could not remain and were rightly apprehensive of reprisals. But this did not diminish in any way their enthusiasm, though they were aware that hostile eyes were watching them, recording every incident.'[7]

In the meantime the engineers were hard at work, and gun emplacements, fuel pumps, stores and the inevitable cable stations were blown up; ammunition and explosive dumps erupted in gigantic pyrotechnics, and nineteen German-chartered caiques were burned. At midnight, with the extra shipping space provided by the Ems barges packed with prisoners, including – to the relief of the islanders – the foremost Quislings, the majority of the force sailed for the nearest S.B.S. base, leaving a rearguard patrol under Stud Stellin to watch and report events and also to distribute among the populace the bulk food the force had brought with them.

By the next afternoon, after a bombing raid and an inept attempt to land German troops directly into the harbour which received a crippling reception at the hands of Stellin's patrol, the Swastika was again flying over the Castello. But the entire raiding force with the exception of the two drowned Greek officers had returned safely to base, only six of them being even slightly wounded; and they had brought with them over 150 prisoners and had left behind 21 German and Italian dead on the island. If it had not been a typical S.B.S operation, it nevertheless maintained the S.B.S. success rate.

The return of Lapraik's squadron with the Greek Sacred Squadron, the Greek collaborators and the German prisoners to the S.B.S. base posed quite a large number of problems, not least that of Turkish neutrality. For in common with the whole string of bases formed in the area since the fall of Cos, this one was deep inside Turkish waters and its size and population could no longer be excused by whimsicalities about engine failure forcing a lone ship to invoke the belligerent's right of forty-eight hours in neutral waters in order to carry out repairs.

Turkey's neutrality, though passionately desired by both her people and her government, had always been difficult to maintain, as is any pose by a weak country judged undesirable by a powerful neighbour. At the beginning of the war, Turkey, unlike Norway and Sweden, had not been particularly affected; but with the invasion of Russia and the capture by the Wehrmacht of the northern shores of the Black Sea, the

presence of so much military power so close entailed greater
subservience to Hitler's wishes than strict neutrality would
allow.

Coal, iron, wood and, most importantly, chrome were
demanded by Berlin in increasing quantities – though paid for
in sound currency – and after 1941, occasional passage of
German naval and mercantile shipping from the Black Sea to
the Aegean; and to Britain's stern complaints on this last
matter Turkish diplomats replied pointing out that they were
not in fact guilty of any infringement of maritime law and
moreover they would have no objection whatsoever to British
shipping passing through the Dardanelles and the Bosphorus
into the Black Sea at any time they wished!

But with the passage of time and the retreat of the German
armies back towards the Carpathians, the German threat to
Turkey lessened, and the influence which the Allies could bring
to bear increased proportionately. Moreover, Turkish
neutrality became valuable to Hitler, and if her evident leaning
towards the Anglo-Americans was a matter for great irritation,
it was not as disastrous as an outright alliance with them would
be, with its threat of the bombing of the Rumanian oil-fields
from Turkish aerodromes.

By the end of 1943, therefore, Turkey's neutrality had
begun to favour the Allied cause, and the length of her almost
unpopulated southern coastline contributed a screen behind
which she could plead ignorance if too hard pressed by
German embassy officials. When they produced air
photographs of what were obviously British naval vessels lying
in Yedi Atalla Bay, for instance, the Turkish official would
promise to investigate, though pointing out that the craft was
probably in there to carry out repairs. When the German
called again later to enquire as to the results of the
investigation, he was told that they had proved negative and
that no British vessels were there.

This would, in fact, be true – since acting on a warning from
a junior Turkish Customs official, the craft would have moved
half a mile away into another bay before the arrival of the
more senior, investigating official. Walter Milner-Barry's
diary is peppered with illuminating references to the minutiae
which such conditions produce:

On 7th March arrived at Penzik on the Turkish mainland at dawn and lay up for the day. The isthmus, at this point, is only half a mile wide or thereabouts, and it seems absurd that we couldn't walk across to Port Deremen ... Rowed across to a waterfall for a bath in fresh water, which was very welcome already.

Rain, but not heavy. Turkish Officer came on board, bringing his own lunch and arak. A very nice fellow ...

I spent a comparatively peaceful day and was able to go ashore and visit a stream of fresh water ... There I encountered a Turkish Officer of unknown rank, who wanted to know what we were doing in Turkish waters. I gave him the stock reply that we had engine trouble on board, but would move as soon as it was cleared up. I took him back with me on board, and gave him a bottle of Syrian arak to seal our neutral friendship.

On the 23rd we moved 'Tewfik' again, advisedly, a few miles east, because a Turkish Officer had again appeared to complain about our still being in the same anchorage ... we had to give him a pair of boots, which are apparently unobtainable in Turkey ... We anchored and tied up within a few feet, literally, of the shore.[8]

Thus was the facade of Turkish neutrality maintained, her relations with Britain and America improved, her attitude to Germany justified – and S.B.S. and Greek Sacred Squadron operations in the Aegean made possible, for Haifa, Cyprus or even Castelorizzo were really too far away for convenience.

As to life in the bases for S.B.S. squadrons, John Lodwick has left by far the strongest evocation.

Picture the deep, indented Gulf of Cos, with uninhabited shores and sullen, fir-covered mountains rising abruptly from the water's edge. In this two hundred miles of coastline it would not be easy for you to find S.B.S., but if you were wise, you would look for some bay screened by small islands suitable for training purposes. Again, if you were wise, you would consult your map in search of one of the few streams from which drinkable water might be drawn.

Entering this bay, you would at first judge it to be empty. Closer inspection would show you a large, squat, ugly schooner lying close to one shore, with her gangplank down and a horde of dories, folboats, rubber dinghies, and rafts nuzzling one flank like kittens about the teats of their mother. Farther off, a full mile

away, lie five or six motor launches and an M.T.B. under
camouflage, and within gin-and-lime distance of them a sleeker,
trimmer, cleaner caique, which is obviously naval property. In
this area, too, are other subsidiary caiques. The intervening water
is dotted with small boats from which men are fishing ... mostly
with grenades.

Let us approach the large and ugly schooner. She is the *Tewfik*
of Port Said, S.B.S. depot ship. In her vast stern a naked figure is
crouching, and whittling at something with a knife. It is Lassen,
and he is making a bow with which to shoot pigs. Down below, in
the murky cabin at the foot of the steep companion-way, David
Sutherland, pipe in mouth, is writing an operational order.
Beside him are rum bottles, magnums of champagne from Nisiros
reserved for special occasions, and a neat list showing the
casualties inflicted on the enemy during the current month ...
and our own.

'Blythe, Captain H.W., plus 4 – out – 4.4.44. Due in 12.4.44.
Overdue. Target, CALCHI.'

Presently, Sutherland reaches a difficult point in his work. He
takes the pipe from his mouth and shouts:–

'Corporal Morris.'

A tall, angular, serious, and bespectacled figure comes bowling
down the companion-way with a file in his hand. Curiously
enough, it is the file which Sutherland wants, for Morris possesses
second sight. Morris retires. His typewriter, seldom silent, begins
clicking again in the distance.

Just forrard of the poop, Sergeant Jenkins, known colloquially
as 'The Soldier's Friend' by reason of his claims to satisfy
everyone, is trying to do three things at once. Sergeant Jenkins is
accusing one S.B.S. man of pinching a tin of sausage meat,
endeavouring to prevent another from doing the same thing
under his very nose, and issuing orders to the Greek cooks
concerning dinner.

'Not octopus again,' he begs them. 'Not octopus, *please!*'

On the hatch beside him, Nobby Clarke, his magnificent
moustache stained by indelible pencil marks, is endeavouring to
write an operational report under difficult conditions. Two
American war correspondents recline on the same hatch in deck-
chairs. They are polishing recently acquired Lugers.

Farther forward, Guardsmen O'Reilly, Conby and D'Arcy,
mugs of rum and tea in their hands, are discussing the good old
days in Libya. In the black hole behind them which is the main
men's quarters, the severe and well-cropped head of Staff-
Sergeant Major John Riley can be seen. Riley, oblivious of the
noisy and vulgar game of pontoon going on in his immediate

neighbourhood, is playing bridge.

In the forepeak, German prisoners, poking their heads up inquisitively, are being given cigarettes by almsgivers.

Towards dusk, the scene becomes more animated, and the immense capacity of the British soldier for slumber less noticeable. The headquarter signallers are pursued, for they alone have news of what is going on in the latest raids ... another is almost certainly setting out to continue them. Men who have been bathing, fishing, bartering with the local Turks, return, demanding supper loudly. Aft, Paddy Errett, Cumper's deputy, is cursing and producing perfectly packed explosive charges at two minutes' notice.

A motor boat chugs alongside, and Sutherland is whisked away to Levant Schooner 9, where Lieutenant-Commander Campbell, sherry glass in hand, is entertaining a couple of M.T.B. skippers with the details of their coming patrol, which, tonight, will be north of Cos. 'E' boats are expected.

Sutherland and Campbell confer, confide, plot, send signals ...

Keith Balsillie is zero-ing a German sniper's rifle found on Piscopi.

Marine Hughes is eating a tin of peaches ...

'Brown Body' Henderson is unable to find any volunteers for P.T.

South of Samos, Harold Chevalier, two days out from base, has just ordered a German caique to heave-to.[9]

It sounds idyllic, of course, though a trifle cramped; and according to Milner-Barry, life aboard a caique or schooner was 'bloody when it rained', which it did quite often.

But it was not to last much longer, for requests had come for S.B.S. squadrons to be based in Italy for operations in Yugoslavia and the Adriatic islands. Moreover, the Greek Sacred Squadron was now adjudged quite capable of taking over the S.B.S. role in the Aegean, where every move forward would take them closer to their own homeland. Ian Lapraik would remain with them to act as adviser and as link with Cairo H.Q., and Sergeant Dale of the S.B.S. would remain attached for Intelligence purposes.

The S.B.S. were moving on.

FIVE

Triumph and Frustration on the Mainland

AUGUST '44—APRIL '45

The squadrons began arriving in Italy on August 11th, 1944 and the following month was spent in the dreary routines of establishing a main base and moving into it. Monte St. Angelo provided a school which could be turned into a main billet, and the surrounding hills and forests of the Gargano peninsula a pleasant enough and useful training area. The L.R.D.G. were already there, so many old friendships were renewed and much good advice received for L.R.D.G. patrols had been operating for some time in Yugoslavia, where they had made close acquaintance with the bravery and comradeship of the ordinary Partisan soldier, and also the obliquity and obstruction of some of their political commissars.

Walter Milner-Barry had preceded them all to Italy and greeted David Sutherland on his arrival with somewhat gloomy prognostications regarding Italian rapacity, lack of interest at headquarters in Bari in S.B.S. or any other Special Service activities, and a somewhat *laisser-faire* attitude among the Royal Navy people he had met so far – in fact, the normal reception accorded to any military formation moving into a new area, as any ex-serviceman will immediately recognise. But by the end of the month, he and other S.B.S. officers and men were regularly crossing the Adriatic in fast M.T.Bs. to make rendezvous with L.R.D.G. or Partisan patrols coming out or just collecting stores, and thereby gaining experience of some of the problems of operating off that rocky and island-studded coast.

On August 27th, Lassen, with a newcomer, Lieutenant J.C. Henshaw, was landed with two patrols just north of the Yugoslav-Albanian border with instructions to interfere with enemy communications in the area, and, as a main operation, to destroy a railway bridge. The salient points of Lassen's report are worth quoting:

3. *NARRATIVE.*
   Landed on night 27/28 Aug 44 at MR 513456 S.W. of GRUDA where LRDG patrol reception party laid on. The party, all total 41 men proceeded by night laying up in daylight, to Target Railway Bridge at MR 619422 which was completely destroyed at 2300 30/31 Aug 44. Arrived next morning at Partisan H.Q. in high mountains at MR 595480 which was considered absolutely safe. On morning of 2 Sept 44, this H.Q. was surrounded by 400 USTACHI and GERMANS and fighting began. Lt. Henshaw with five men defended one ridge. Later a withdrawal was ordered and carried out successfully except for 1 RE who was taken prisoner together with 2 L.R.D.G. personnel after a 3 hr fight.

   SBS patrols and 2 remaining LRDG personnel successfully evacuated on night 5/6 Sept 44.

4. *INTELLIGENCE.*
   Partisans are very brave and efficient raiders in this area. Number 40 altogether, and do much small scale raiding on roads and rails. Nearly all enemy troops are USTACHI who are highly trained and skilled in anti-Partisan and anti-SBS work. They are very good.[1]

That the Ustachi should win praise from Lassen is hardly surprising for they were recruited from among the Croat peoples, who throughout history have gained a reputation for producing superb soldiers – but according to Henshaw, even they must have been astonished by the performance of Lassen and the men he led. One of the instructors at Achnacarry had previously remarked upon Lassen's extraordinarily fast reaction time and his almost miraculous ability to move swiftly 'as if without touching the ground', and on this occasion, according to Henshaw, he seemed to be everywhere at once – and always where danger threatened most. He was invariably followed closely by Shaun O'Reilly and others of his own patrol, and between them they so shocked the attackers with their onslaught that in the evening these withdrew, leaving a gap through which Lassen took his men back to the coastline, where in due course they were met by the navy and evacuated.

Jellicoe later ordered Lassen to submit a fuller report, especially with regard to the destruction of the railway bridge. 'Ve landed. Ve reached the bridge. Ve destroyed it,' Lassen grumbled. 'Vat else is there to say?' – exhibiting a disdain for paperwork which will excite the sympathy of a large number of soldiers; but also exhibiting a growing acerbity, as battle fatigue began to erode even his placidity and charm.

Other S Squadron patrols were dropped into the area or sent in by sea, but found themselves up against two new and disconcerting factors. Firstly, they were operating on a continent instead of an island, so there was no surrounding sea across which help or re-supply could come from any angle; secondly, they were no longer operating in a friendly environment where the natives not only greeted and helped them with enthusiasm, but also could be depended upon to maintain at least a 95% screen of security.

These beneficial factors no longer obtained, for if the Partisan leaders were not actually prepared to betray Allied plans to the Germans if they did not forward their own immediate political ends, they were certainly prepared to use every obstructive ploy they could concoct to prevent operations which might adversely affect their own local prestige. As a result, and to the perplexity of many S.B.S. men who thought that the only possible attitude towards the Germans would be of unmixed hostility, they found on occasion that the local guerilla bands were so bleakly unco-operative that there was no practical alternative but to abort the whole mission, return home and start off again entirely on their own.

The S.B.S. officer who most thoroughly appreciated the new conditions was Lieutenant Ambrose McGonigal, who landed in southern Yugoslavia at the end of August and made not the slightest attempt to inform the local Partisans of his plans. As a result they had to tail along behind in order to discover his intentions, from which position, after a long night march, they watched him blow in a railway tunnel and thoroughly wreck nearby installations, having first dispersed the Chetnik guard with Bren-gun fire. He then moved with his party further inland and spent the next two weeks ambushing German patrols – and when more and larger patrols were sent out to investigate the disturbances, ambushing them too. His sense of timing would seem to have been impeccable, for when eventually he withdrew – leaving behind several thoroughly exasperated Partisan commissars – he and his men had killed or wounded well over fifty German soldiers and an unknown number of Chetniks, derailed a train and thoroughly disorganised the local German command – all in addition to the original tunnel destroyed – for the loss of only one man, killed in the last engagement.

Nonetheless, the atmosphere in which the S Squadron patrols had had to live and operate was vastly different from that to which they had been used. Many of them longed for the sound of Greek voices again, and for the feeling of trust and co-operation they had left behind them in the Greek islands.

Ian Patterson brought L Squadron up into Italy during the first half of September.

They had been by no means idle since he had withdrawn them from Turkish waters, indeed they had undertaken the annual raid on Crete, though on this occasion they had confused the enemy by concentrating on the destruction of fuel instead of aircraft. Advance reconnaissance parties had been put ashore early in July – and immediately, of course, encountered the usual phenomenon.

'The general tone for security throughout this operation,' reads Patterson's report, 'was set upon the arrival of the advance party in the east of the island, by the totally unnecessary appearance of twenty-three mules and their attendant villagers.'

Nevertheless, planning and operations continued uninterrupted. The main parties arrived, were briefed and guided to their objectives, and on July 23rd, 165,000 gallons of petrol in seven different dumps went up in vast eruptions of flame and smoke. David Clark's party were slightly inconvenienced when two German guards came across them and, like the *Unteroffizier* on Simi, refused to accept David's suggestion of surrender.

'... One of them, however, shouted something so I shot him twice with my carbine. Corporal Bentley shot the second man. It was all highly unpleasant and inconvenient ...'

Within a week all parties had been successfully evacuated and were on their way back to Egypt, missing only two men: Captain Lodwick and Bombardier Nixon, who had been taken prisoner and were thus to be absent from S.B.S. operations for some time. They were taken first to Athens, then to Salonika, then up into Serbia, where they eventually escaped to join up with a local band of guerillas, then spent some time in, of all places, Sofia.

Oh, yes, prison life can have its moments ... once you know that you will eventually escape. After 134 days we return to the unit.

'Ah, you're back,' said Jellicoe. 'Damned slow about it, weren't you?'[2]

Being so 'damned slow' Lodwick missed what was arguably the most successful operation ever carried out by Special Service troops.

Walter Milner-Barry had now rather reluctantly taken command of H.Q. Squadron. It brought him a majority (unpaid, as it was not 'on establishment'), but he could no longer deny the reality that he was too old to be offered command of an operational squadron. In this respect, however, his position did give him news of all suggested operations for the S.B.S., and if some of the grander projects did come off – such as the idea of dropping the whole formation into the north of Istria to attack enemy lines of communication and then possibly attempt to block the inevitable German retreat back to Austria – he was pretty certain that he could insert himself somewhere into a more active role than that of counting blankets and issuing ammunition.

He need not have worried. His diary for September 22nd reads:

Spent the morning on chores in the office. Things are pretty well organised now and the garrison engineer is going to try to get piping for laying hot water. Basketball in the afternoon, during which a dramatic message was brought to me telling me to go to Bari. So left about 5.00 in a 3 tonner and got in after a most uncomfortable journey, about 10.00. There, a scene of indescribable confusion, as L Squadron are being sent to seize and hold Araxos aerodrome in Northern Peloponnese ...[3]

S Squadron were out of luck; it was L Squadron who were going back to Greece.

It had been evident for some time that the German hold on Greece was becoming ever more tenuous, and by September 1944, the vast threat to the German homeland posed by the Red Armies as they drove westwards through Bulgaria, Rumania and Poland, was such that every able-bodied and trained soldier was needed back on the home front. Moreover, with the defeat of Germany evidently little but a matter of time, the Greek security battalions formed from Axis collaborators were wavering in their loyalty to such an extent that it was less faithfulness to their promises of support to the *Wehrmacht* than fear of what would happen to them at the hands of the guerilla armies of E.L.A.S. which kept them at their posts.

Meanwhile in London, Mr. Churchill was aching to see measures taken which would free Greece from Hitler's domination but also preserve her from Stalin's. Five thousand men, he recommended, should be available to land at the Piraeus as soon as the liberation of Athens became a viable operation; but where in the Mediterranean area were there now one thousand men, let alone five, not already committed. to action on one front or another? They would have to be British troops, too, for Mr. Stimson's strictures against American participation in colonial expansionist activities still held sway in Washington.

But while the bottom of every manpower barrel between Baghdad and Algiers was being scraped for troops, at least this time the need for air-cover was not forgotten; fighter squadrons from Italy would be made available to protect *Operation Manna* – as the liberation of Greece was dubbed almost before the identity of the first platoon of troops had been decided upon – and at the same time they would be available for attacks on German shipping attempting to bring out those isolated garrisons on the Aegean islands.

But where would the fighter squadrons be based?

Jellicoe had been brought into the discussions almost from their beginning (which gave him little more notice than he had had for his descent upon Rhodes), and various paragraphs of his report make fascinating reading:

3. Operation TOWANBUCKET was therefore conceived, planned and mounted on the lightest possible scale. Although the inevitable 'snowball' was eventually produced (two companies of H.L.I. and later the whole battalion joined exiguous BUCKETFORCE), this operation by which the first allied force re-entered GREECE since our evacuation in APRIL 1941 was throughout executed (and circumscribed) by a rigorous economy of means.

4. After some hesitation between the alternative attractions of KALAMATA and ARAXOS the decision was taken to capture ARAXOS airfield in the NW corner of the PELOPONNESE. The operation was christened TOWANBUCKET for reasons best known to the Inter-Service Secretariat of H.Q., B.A.F., the heterogeneous forces designated for the operation were labelled BUCKETFORCE and I was put in command.

5. BUCKETFORCE comprised a cross-section of the hybrid units under command of H.Q., L.F.A. and H.Q., B.A.F. ranging from L Squadron S.B.S., 2908 Squadron R.A.F. regiment, one patrol L.R.D.G., one section No. 40 Royal Marine Commando, to R.A.F. ground and maintenance personnel and an R.N./C.O.P.P. party – in all some 450 curiously assorted all ranks ...

BUCKETFORCE was subsequently strengthened by two companies 2 H.L.I. (and eventually by the whole battalion) and by a strong platoon of British and American war correspondents.[4]

It was during the somewhat hectic development of this situation that Milner-Barry joined the 'scene of indescribable confusion' and discovered in more detail what was afoot. Charles Bimrose and his patrol had already been dropped into the hills just south of Araxos and had reported that the airfield appeared clear of enemy troops – certainly of enough enemy troops seriously to interfere with a landing of squadron size – but that the port of Patras was still held in strength; but speed, as so often in military affairs, was of the essence.

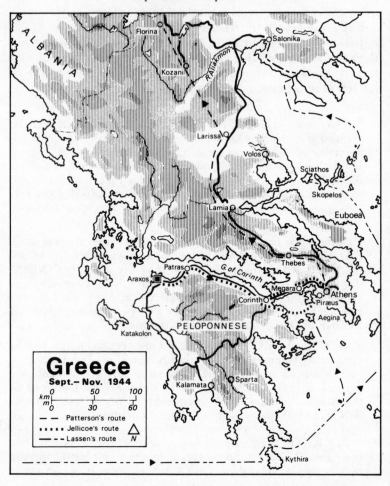

This was, indeed, thoroughly appreciated, and during the morning of September 23rd, Patterson and fifty-eight of his men with their weapons and equipment were crammed into six Dakotas and sent off, arriving over Araxos and dropping down at Bimrose's signal with no trouble save 'that the stores were scattered over a wide area, took considerable time being located, and when found had been comprehensively looted by the Greek villagers.'

The first task for the majority of the men was to carry out,

with the help of the same villagers, some urgent repairs to the
runways, and for Patterson to ensure their protection from
attack while doing so. Having found that there were, in fact,
no signs of enemy presence in the area, he sent patrols out first
along the main Patras road to secure a bridge (it was already
blown), and then others south towards Katakolon, the port
where it was hoped to land the seaborne element of
Bucketforce – 'much used', according to Jellicoe, 'by the
FRANKISH Crusaders for the invasion of the
PELOPONNESE.'

The following day, September 24th, the main force came
flooding in. Jellicoe himself, accompanied by Milner-Barry
and Kenneth Fox, flew into the repaired airstrip to find that
more Dakotas loaded with stores had already arrived plus
eight Spitfires, that Squadron-Leader Wynne with his R.A.F.
Regiment contingent were disembarking successfully down at
Katakolon, and that Ian Patterson had sent David Clark and
two patrols to investigate the situation in and around Patras.

It was, according to David, somewhat abstruse. The
E.L.A.S. forces reputedly investing the place were doing so in
a noticeably casual manner, their dominant purpose
apparently being more to impress the local Greeks with their
power and importance than to discommode the German forces
in Patras, their hostility directed almost entirely
against the members of the Greek Security Battalion who were
holding the eastern side of the town. However, a great deal of
information was available to Patterson when he came up
regarding the situation inside the town itself, for another of the
incredibly brave and ubiquitous M.O.4 officers, Captain
Gray, had lived in and around Patras for over a year and could
supply accurate details of German strengths and locations.

Moreover, the Swedish Red Cross representative, Herr
Ornstroder, was anxious to prevent battle and bloodshed
inside Patras, and his first contact with Patterson was to
suggest that the German commandant, *Kapitän zur Zee*
Magnus, might consider terms for a capitulation. In view of
the fact that from Gray's account it seemed that the Patras
defences were manned by some 850-900 Germans plus the
1,600 men of the Greek Security Battalion, whereas Patterson
had only 62 fighting effectives under his own command and
could hope for reinforcement by only another 300 at most (and

that only by denuding Araxos), this proposition held great attractions, but by the time Jellicoe came up it began to look as though *Kapitän* Magnus was merely procrastinating.

Perhaps, Patterson suggested, they should now concentrate on the Greek Security Battalion who were undoubtedly more than willing to desert the German cause, provided they could be guaranteed British protection not only for themselves but also for the civilians of Patras, a strongly anti-E.L.A.S. bastion. Their commander, Colonel Courkalakos, was more than willing to enter discussions, although as Jellicoe reported:

> These negotiations dragged, in a way peculiar to GREECE in general and the PELOPONNESE in particular, for several days during which time COURKALAKOS tried to secure better terms ... fully cognisant of our numerical weakness, but almost embarrassingly anxious to extricate themselves from an untenable and unenviable position.[5]

While the negotiations dragged, Patterson had perforce to engage German attention by switching his patrols from position to position in the manner of a stage army, maintaining a constant show of force against the town and especially the harbour area, in a display in which noise was more important than strike power. As John Lodwick describes it:

> From a wooden ridge, David Clark made a brave show with his mortars. 'Up a trifle, Sergeant Chambers ... no, no, no ... you hit a cowshed that time ... left a bit.'
> Mortars had never played an important part in S.B.S. weapon-training curriculum.[6]

But by October 1st Jellicoe's patience was wearing thin, and in any case tactical factors necessitated action. On his instructions, Captain Gray informed Courkalakos that although the British sympathised with him and wished to help, Colonel Jellicoe could accept no responsiblity for the safety of the men of the Security Battalion except for those who handed in their arms by 0600 the following morning; Patterson, Jellicoe and Milner-Barry, who had now come up to join them, then discussed what arrangements to make for

the reception and made bets upon the likely number. No
estimate exceeded 300 ...

> It was therefore to our astonishment and considerable
> embarrassment that masses of Greeks began flocking in to our
> assembly points from 2000 hours that night ... By daybreak 1600
> personnel in all had surrendered and their disposal became a
> grave problem.[7]

But it also offered a magnificent opportunity, for the Greeks
had been holding the whole of the eastern edge of the town
and such had been the secrecy of their withdrawal that *Kapitän*
Magnus and his men were wholly unaware of the open flank
they had left. Patterson struck immediately, and almost
within minutes two armoured cars and some jeeps containing
twenty mixed R.A.F. and S.B.S. men were probing in towards
the centre of the town. They had already reached the market-
place before the Germans reacted, driving them out again
after a violent exchange in which a great deal of ammunition
was expended by both sides without, however, causing any
British casualties.

It was obvious by now that Patras was fast becoming an
untenable position for the Germans, and during the daylight
hours of October 2nd and 3rd Jellicoe arranged for that fact
to be hammered home. Squadron-Leader Wynne brought up
more of his R.A.F. Regiment platoons who pushed into the
southern suburbs with admirable gallantry and enterprise,
and Patterson and two S.B.S. patrols drove the enemy off one
of the slight hills on the outskirts and captured a 76mm. gun
which they promptly turned on the port area itself, sinking a
Siebel ferry apparently crowded with troops.

By the time darkness had fallen on October 3rd, it was plain
that the Germans were getting out – but, of course, with their
usual efficiency. Jellicoe's instructions to his combined R.A.F.
and S.B.S. teams to force their way through and into the
harbour area and thus prevent wide-scale demolitions were
obeyed to the limit of the strength available, but in spite of
this, the Germans held their perimeter until the last moment
and were aboard their craft and gone in twenty minutes,
leaving under the more important port installations prepared
charges which were fortunately found and de-fused in time.

'Triumphal entry at 8.00 *a.m.*,' Milner-Barry recorded,

> ... with George [Jellicoe] and ELAS Brigade Commander in the
> first jeep, with the Union Jack and Greek flag flying. Terrific
> reception, carpet on the streets, flowers and lovely girls on
> balconies. Drove the second jeep myself with Achilles, the
> Capitanos, and more Greeks.[8]

This sort of reception was to be repeated wherever they
went in Greece, unless it was into an area dominated by
E.L.A.S., and there it was obvious that the local population
wished ardently to follow the usual pattern but were afraid to
do so. On one occasion, Jellicoe actually overheard an E.A.M.
official upbraiding a Greek farmer for his evident desire to
welcome the British who had just liberated his village from the
Germans, and abusing him for offering them hospitality.

If all was relaxation and delight inside Patras, along the
road to the east and the stretch of water bordering it, all was
speed and excitement. From Patras a fleet of German craft of
varying sizes was now making its way through the narrows
and into the Gulf of Corinth, obviously bound for the Corinth
Canal and the Piraeus – and Patterson and his men set off to
hinder it as much as possible. The captured 76mm. gun was
hitched to Patterson's jeep, and, followed by other jeeps and a
3-tonner, they all set off on an exciting but perilous chase.

Patterson, never a cautious driver, rocketed crazily along
precipitous mountain roads, slewing his vehicle and its
unwieldy attachment around the caverns left by German
demolitions, followed by his delighted patrols and later by an
impressed Milner-Barry, who came up with them just as they
had stopped on a headland with the German ships sailing
along below.

> Had two shots at the ships, during which the gun straddled
> them, but the .5s (on the jeeps) couldn't quite reach. Jerries
> stopped their ships, got in a huddle, and then fired into the air,
> thinking they were being bombed. The gun had no sight, so it was
> guesswork, with Ian ramming the shells in with an iron bar.
> Enormous fun![9]

Patterson's comment was a little more restrained:

It was not altogether satisfactory as the Germans had removed the sights. However, by a process of hit or miss, we succeeded in inflicting casualties; many of them due, I have no doubt, to shock.[10]

But the German demolitions delayed them more and more as they advanced along the road, and it was not until October 7th that they reached Corinth, to exchange desultory fire with Germans on the far side of the canal and take the surrender of another Greek Security Battalion. On the representation of an accredited official of the Greek government who had arrived at Patras, a small detachment of the R.A.F. men was then dispatched to Sparta to take surrender of yet another battalion. Too great a proportion of Bucketforce was being detached for prison camp organisation and protecting the inhabitants from their political rivals.

The S.B.S. sections, however, were all still racing eastwards. After Corinth they used an improvised ferry to cross to the north side, and then swung around to reach Megara where the force was split. Charles Bimrose took three patrols on foot up into the hills towards Thebes in a gallant attempt to cut off a substantial part of the German rearguard, but the Germans were still Germans; coolly and efficiently they retired with precision and professionalism, and nothing would deflect them from their iron code. After a few days Bimrose accepted that a spirit of opportunism would not be enough, and he withdrew his small force and left the *Wehrmacht* to continue its systematic withdrawal.

Keith Balsillie, however, detached with one patrol by caique to the far side of the Bay of Salamis, successfully landed at Scaramanga and pressed onward to become the first uniformed Allied soldier freely to enter the Piraeus since its fall to the Germans in 1941.

These detachments obviously left Patterson very short of men at Megara – barely sufficient, in fact, to fulfil their latest allocated task, that of covering the landing-ground during the arrival of the vital reinforcements; these alone would keep *Operation Manna* alive, for with their repulse of Bimrose's patrols, the German rearguard had begun to realise the weakness of their opponents and had started to strike back. All through the daylight hours of October 11th the two sides manoeuvred for position and fought tiny patrol actions, and by the time darkness fell they were thoroughly mixed up – so much so that when, to Patterson's enormous relief, the first company of the 4th Parachute Battalion with their commanding officer, Lieutenant-Colonel Coxon, dropped on to the Megara landing-strip, German patrols were trapped between the two British forces and at least twenty-four taken prisoner.

Friday, October 13th, would seem to have been more unlucky for the Germans than the British – though only by the fact of their withdrawal from Athens for they did so almost unmolested. Under orders of Lieutenant-Colonel Coxon, Jellicoe and Milner-Barry were now instructed to find out exactly what was happening in the Greek capital, the latter being brought up for the purpose from Patras early that morning.

Lovely drive along the Gulf of Corinth. Stopped at Corinth for a word with the H.L.I. as the canal was well and truly blocked with ships and blown. Stopped again at Loutraki for a bite of bully with 'L' rear H.Q., then on to Megara. Showered with flowers and grapes. At Megara found the gliders about to land; a great sight. Yesterday the parachutists had 25 casualties owing to gusty wind, some being dragged for miles and only stopped by jeeps. Brig. Tohig said George must get into Athens somehow, and assume control, and handed him his own red tabs to wear if necessary. It was agreed that George should be a brigadier, and myself a full colonel, so we donned the necessary emblems.

Information about Athens was very conflicting, so rather timidly embarked in a motorboat with George, Bill Reid, Shan Sidgwick, and Cpl. Newton as escort, about 5.00, and went over to the Salamis shore. Flares, shots, and explosions all around Eleusis made the scene rather eerie. Decided to swim if shot up from the shore, but landed without incident and promptly hid in a ditch until we heard obviously Greek voices.

Just beyond Eleusis contacted Ian Patterson. He and George bicycled into Athens, the rest following in cars.

Reception by Greeks was overwhelming; tears, shouts, kisses, handshakes, blows on the back, dragged into houses and nearly suffocated. Made a speech from a balcony, shouting 'Zeto to ELAS,' when I ought to have said 'Hellas' meaning 'Up with Greece,' rather than 'Up with Elas' but I don't think the loss of an H was remarked on in the excitement.

Eventually arrived with three others, on the back of a motorbike outside the Grande Bretagne, there to be fervently embraced by my old friend Catsotas ... Entering the hotel I was greeted by the Swiss Manager as though I had left the day before, and invited to sign my name in the register, immediately after General Falkenhausen, who had left, it seems a few hours before.[11]

Saturday, October 14th, 1944, was the day Athens celebrated her liberation after three and a half years of German occupation, and in that celebration L Squadron, S.B.S., were involved to a notable extent. Jellicoe, Milner-Barry and Patterson were continually called upon to appear on balconies outside the Grande Bretagne (in which the bulk of the squadron was housed in unaccustomed luxury) and to make speeches in a mixture of Greek and English which quickly became thoroughly acceptable to everyone. Some of them attended a moving and magnificent *Te Deum* Mass conducted at the Cathedral by Archbishop Damaskinos, soon to become Regent of Greece in the King's absence.

As for more junior members of the squadron, they were swept up in a positive torrent of exultation and hospitality which lasted for three days and left some of them decidedly pallid beneath their tans. Not that they were ungrateful. 'The Greeks,' one of them was heard to say reflectively, 'are all right!'

Perhaps it was a commanding officer's natural concern for the welfare of his men, perhaps there were tactical factors to be considered, but after those three days Colonel Jellicoe (the rank of brigadier lasted only a very short time) decreed that L Squadron must move on. David Clark with two patrols was sent by caique out of Piraeus, around the point and up through the Euboea Channel towards Lamia in the hope of cutting off a large number of the retreating Germans, while the main strength of what was now called *Pompforce*, consisting of the 4th Parachute Battalion, some paratroop engineers, some of the R.A.F. Regiment, one battery of 75mm. guns and the remainder of the S.B.S., drove north up the road behind them.

Lamia was soon passed with little sign of even the German rearguard, though these had left their mark on the road in the shape of innumerable demolitions and quite a number of cunning booby-traps. There were also signs of significant successes by marauding Spitfires: abandoned equipment, dead horses and mules, and hastily dug graves marked with a wooden cross and coal-skuttle helmet. But it was not until Pompforce had driven through Larissa and across the River Aliakmon that they came across defences deployed and manned to keep them back, just south of the small town of Kozani.

Pompforce now split, Lieutenant-Colonel Coxon taking his battalion around in a hook to by-pass Kozani and drive for Florina, thus cutting off the Germans; Ian Patterson with his own men, the R.A.F. companies, the engineers and the artillery mounting a frontal attack aimed at holding German attention and perhaps in due course driving them up into Coxon's waiting arms.

Patterson's attack was put in at dawn and, looked at from the point of view of the prevalent infantry doctrine, it cannot be said to have been either organised or launched upon prescribed lines. There was no artillery cover for the first advance owing to the fact that the battery of field guns was still moving into position; the R.A.F. contingent, though they advanced with admirable dash, soon found themselves beyond radio control (which was in any case unreliable as a result of a sudden rainstorm); and the S.B.S. found themselves pinned down in open ground, their leading patrol caught behind minuscule rocks and unable to move for over two hours.

It was all very uncomfortable for a lot of people for quite a long time, and much caustic comment was passed upon the situation both then and later – but the impasse was suddenly resolved by the unexpected conjunction of several events. Firstly, the field guns came into belated action against the German positions; then an S.B.S. mortar-bomb landed with unexpected accuracy plumb into a German heavy machine-gun post which had hitherto held a commanding field of fire; and at the same time – most conclusive factor of all – reports reached the German commander of the movement of Coxon's paratroopers, and he realised that if he and his men were to reach the Yugoslav frontier safely they must move out immediately.

By late evening Kozani had been liberated, Patterson's force was through and driving for Florina where they linked up with their Pompforce partners, then to their annoyance to receive orders to proceed no further into Yugoslavia or Albania, as their sudden appearance might further complicate the already difficult conditions under which Sutherland was still trying to operate.

They also received news of Andy Lassen who had now been promoted to command M Squadron in Ian Lapraik's place, and who had been moving parallel to them on the right flank.

Lassen and his men had, in fact, been island-hopping up through the northern Sporades, and in doing so had slightly impinged upon the agreed operational area of the Greek Sacred Squadron. This matter having been amicably adjusted, Lassen landed at both Skopelos and Sciathos and then put Lieutenant Martin Solomon, his naval liaison officer and firm friend, into Volos on the mainland. Here, according to John Lodwick, occurred one of those incidents which might partly explain the bewilderment with which the English are so often regarded by foreigners. While on land, Solomon was approached by an immaculately clad British major.

'He had come down from some mountain or other,' said Solomon, 'where he had been sitting, apparently forgotten, for over a year. He seemed unsurprised to see us and said "Hullo, Navy, just the fellows I want to see. I have got 10,000 Italians I want you to take off my hands at once. When can you embark them?"'

Martin Solomon pointed to his tiny caique and said diffidently that he could manage four if that would help.

'How long have you had these men?' he asked curiously.

'Oh, since the armistice with Italy, old boy. Damned nuisance they are, too. Still, can't let them starve, I suppose.' Producing a particularly filthy flask of oyzo from his pocket, the major offered Solomon a nip.

Wondering how the major could have fed, clothed, and hidden what amounted to the strength of an infantry division in enemy-occupied country for over a year, Solomon asked him if he spoke Italian.

'Good God, no, old boy,' he replied, looking insulted. 'I'm a sapper.'[12]

What happened to the major and his charges is unrevealed, but from Volos Solomon collected two schooners and orders for Lassen to proceed immediately northwards to investigate the situation in Salonika. Lassen was also sent a jeep to aid his investigations, which pleased him inordinately, and within forty-eight hours M Squadron under their extraordinary commander were all well into northern Greek coastal waters, their craft unnoticed amid a fleet of Greek caiques and miscellaneous shipping.

'I knew what was coming,' Martin Solomon later reported, 'and prepared myself for it all night with prayer and solemn reflection.'

The following morning the two of them landed with the jeep and spent the day on an eighty-mile drive through the surrounding countryside, of which the dominant points were still in German hands though the district in general was fast falling under E.L.A.S. control. Lassen, who had no interest in political doctrines of whatever colour and still less in national sensitivities, then found himself approached by the local guerilla leaders with suggestions which completely bewildered him, though only momentarily. The guerillas proposed that he should curb his curiosity as to conditions in the interior, and even more his activities there – for although he and his men were quite welcome especially if they were bringing extra weapons and ammunition for the guerillas themselves, he should consider himself under E.L.A.S. orders, remain aboard his ship until sent for, and certainly engage in no hostile moves against the Germans without permission, especially as the Germans were preparing to evacuate the district anyway.

Once he had recovered from his astonishment, Lassen's reaction was brusque. He would, he informed the outraged commissar, go where he pleased, see whatever he wished, and if the guerilla leaders and their followers did not want him to attack the Germans, then the best way to secure this end would be to attack them themselves and thus save him the trouble – and why weren't they doing so in full strength already?

To this suggestion the E.L.A.S. forces reacted negatively, as they wished to conserve their ammunition and martial ardour for the civil war they intended to launch as soon as the

Germans were gone, during which they hoped to impose a Communist dictatorship upon their unwilling fellow-countrymen; so after delivering himself of a scarifying tirade upon such matters as Balkan duplicity in general and personal poltroonery in particular, Lassen dismissed the convocation, disembarked his entire force, and during the next few hours dispersed them widely throughout the district with orders to make as much display of presence as they could in order to persuade the Germans that they were surrounded and that the intelligent course for them would be to surrender.

In this he was unsuccessful, for the Germans were far too intent upon returning to the Fatherland for such an alternative as a prison camp to be at all attractive – but at least Lassen and his men could hasten their retreat. Discovering that the western half of Salonika was virtually undefended but that the E.L.A.S. forces had no intention of moving in until the city was completely empty of the enemy, Lassen solved the problem of transporting fifty men there by sequestering four of the local fire-engines and racing through the streets towards the area where the Germans were preparing their usual valedictory demolitions. He caught them completely by surprise, but unfortunately for the Germans their automatic reaction was to snatch up their rifles or race for their machine-gun posts. Lassen's men then worked off the frustration in which E.L.A.S. had bound them since their arrival with fifteen minutes of violent action in which the Germans suffered some sixty casualties.

S.B.S. lost not a single man but when they returned, somewhat jauntily, towards the centre of the town, they noticed a peculiar phenomenon. When they had entered Salonika it had been through deserted streets occasionally hung with Red Flags, but as they made their way back the same streets were crowded with excited men and women who threw flowers at them, offered them drinks of oyzo and domestica, and enthusiastically waved Greek National flags or hastily made Union Jacks.

Much later an analysis of the Greek campaign was written, based upon reports gathered from M.O.4 sources, from the main battle accounts and from agents. It included the following passage:

But for Lassen and his band, Salonika would not have been evacuated as soon as the 30th October 1944. The town would have suffered greater destruction. His solitary jeep and few troops were seen everywhere; behind the enemy's lines, with E.L.A.S., and in the mountains. Their numbers and strength were magnified into many hundreds of men and automatic weapons. Prisoners taken confirmed this, their estimate never being less than one thousand men.[13]

During November, S.B.S. patrols gradually made their separate ways back to Athens where they found instant popularity among the citizens, despite their shabby appearance and worn and unpolished footwear – in such contrast to that of the newly arrived administrative echelons with smartly accoutred officers and strong opinions on the correct angle at which military headgear should be worn. Much oyzo, retsina and domestica were drunk, several engagements between S.B.S. soldiers and Greek girls appeared in regimental orders, and there is reason to believe that quite a few less regular liaisons were also established.

Parties to these arrangements were saddened by the announcement of the departure of L Squadron from Athens on December 8th, 1944, and were thus perhaps at first delighted when, even as the patrols stood waiting to board the aircraft taking them to Italy, the move was abruptly cancelled and they were ordered back to Athens.

But the delight did not last long for the change in plan had been brought about by the decision by E.A.M. not to abide by the agreement to hand in their arms, but to use them instead for the purpose for which they had long intended them: to force a Communist dictatorship on the Greek people before the Western Powers could proceed with their ridiculous and infantile ideas of free elections. As a result, and to their horror, many S.B.S. men found themselves engaged upon that depressing duty for soldiers, 'aid to the civil power', in which they had to hold strongpoints on Athenian streets, regard anyone who approached them as potential enemy regardless of age or sex, and on occasion open fire upon Greeks – a race for whom they had in general nothing but admiration and affection.

To everyone's relief, however, this confrontation lasted only

until January 8th, 1945, at the end of which the E.L.A.S.
forces withdrew from Athens in the face of a build-up of
British orthodox forces, which in turn gave the Athenian
population the security and confidence to express their intense
dislike of all that E.L.A.S. stood for.

The men of L Squadron could also now withdraw; but,
alas, without their beloved commander, for S.B.S. had entered
its second term of tragedy and misfortune.

It had begun during Lassen's journey up to Salonika, when he
had detached Bob Bury in a caique to make contact with one
or other of the guerilla groups along the mainland coast which
were normally engaged in fighting each other. Whether the
wrong group were now in possession of that particular bay, or
whether the right group were there but did not recognise the
approaching craft as friendly is immaterial. They opened fire
on the caique, hit the helmsman in the first strike, and when
Bury leapt up to take his place he was almost immediately
mortally wounded – to be buried next day by the same men
who had killed him, whose identity even then remained
something of a mystery.

It was among Lassen's squadron, too, that the next tragedy
occurred.

By the end of November it had become evident that the
German garrison on Crete was concentrating in a small area
along the north-west section of the coastline between Suda
Bay and Maleme, preparatory to evacuation whenever this
could be organised. Lassen, with M Squadron, landed at
Heraklion on December 3rd, and found the circumstances on
the island similar to those to which they had become
accustomed on the Greek mainland. E.L.A.S. *Andartes* were
somewhat lackadaisically investing the German conclave,
occasionally engaging in Black Market negotiations with
them, and awaiting their unimpeded departure with the
expectation of scavenging arms and supplies from their
discards after they had gone.

Shortly after M Squadron's arrival, Lieutenant Henshaw
penetrated the German perimeter under a flag of truce and
interviewed the commandant, who admitted that his position
was embarrassing and that he would be happy to surrender –

but only to a British force strong enough to protect him and his men from the Cretan populace. Until the appearance of such a British force, he regretted that his garrison must retain their arms for the purposes of self-protection; but in the meantime there was not the slightest reason for aggressive activity by either side – in fact, in order to alleviate boredom and keep up the spirits of all concerned, could they not arrange a football match?

Lassen's reaction to this was apparently to become almost inarticulate with rage, but in order to exert pressure of some sort on the enemy, a certain amount of organisation became necessary. To bring this about, he sent Captain Clynes and Lieutenant Bimrose off in a jeep, with one of the attached Intelligence officers in the back and Private Cornthwaite as a motorcyclist outrider.

They travelled slowly and openly, their uniforms and their transport obviously British; but as they drove along the road between Heraklion and Rethimnon, an E.L.A.S. sniper fired upon them killing the outrider immediately, his second shot passing first through Bimrose's calf and then right through Clynes's body. He died a week later in Athens.

But the third tragedy was the most shattering. A few days before Christmas it became necessary for Ian Patterson to pay a flying visit to the Monte St. Angelo base to check up on such recondite matters as pay and promotions for some of his men, and, more importantly, their future employment. The Dakota took off quite smoothly from the Athens airport, but ran into a complicated weather pattern over the Straits of Otranto which apparently caused an error in navigation ... and after crossing the Italian coast south of Bari, the plane crashed into a hillside, killing everyone on board with the exception of one of the crew.

Stewart Macbeth arrived at the site of the accident some thirty-six hours later to save Patterson from a communal grave, but when the news reached the men of L Squadron they were stunned. The caution with which Patterson had been regarded during his first operations had long been replaced by deep respect, and the devotion he had inspired was such that over half his squadron were to write letters of commiseration to his mother.

Another departure from the S.B.S. about this time, though in much happier circumstances, was of the man who had commanded them ever since their reformation after Stirling's disappearance from the scene. Lieutenant-Colonel George Jellicoe had formed and led them for so long now that it was for many almost impossible to envisage the existence of the unit without him; but the army has realistic precepts upon how long an officer, however gifted, should remain in the same appointment, and now there was a vacancy for him on a new course just about to begin at the Staff College at Haifa.

There was only one possible choice as his successor – the senior member of S.B.S., not only in rank but also in service: David Sutherland.

Sutherland faced an unenviable task. The loss of such key figures in the squadrons would obviously have a dampening effect for some time, but time would pass and new recruits, both commissioned and non-commissioned, were always coming forward – though perhaps after five years of war Britain was no longer able to produce men of the same quality. But the main problem was the atmosphere in which operations now had to be carried out, bedevilled as they were by the politics of the northern Balkan states and the suspicion and fear with which they were surrounded.

In Yugoslavia during the opening weeks of 1945, S.B.S. patrols found their activities so limited that they were virtually penned into the harbour area of the port of Zara – not by German or even Italian forces, but by the orders of the local Yugoslav leader. The latter made it quite clear that none but his own forces and administrators might take credit for the supplies of food and clothing that were now pouring into the port – from the western capitalist countries, be it said – for the relief of the local population. Neither did he wish it to be believed that any but his own battalions had contributed to the expulsion of the Fascist forces from the region, despite the fact that many locals had actually witnessed men wearing British uniforms in action against the enemy. Those who persisted in such testimony found themselves despatched inland, many never to return.

Against this sad and sordid background, the S.B.S. men and their now inveterate comrades of the R.A.F. Regiment waited in grim and cynical mood for further employment, and were relieved when orders came for them to expedite the German evacuation of those jagged splinters of land off the Croatian coastlines which rejoiced in such names as Krk, Rab and Pag, Lussin and Olib. Though the islands themselves were different in almost every way from those in the Aegean which had recently formed the S.B.S. hunting-ground, the garrisons often consisted of the same men – or at least those who had managed escape or evacuation. They were thus experienced and well aware of both the strengths and the weaknesses of the raiding forces now about to attack them, and their defences were both well conceived and soundly constructed.

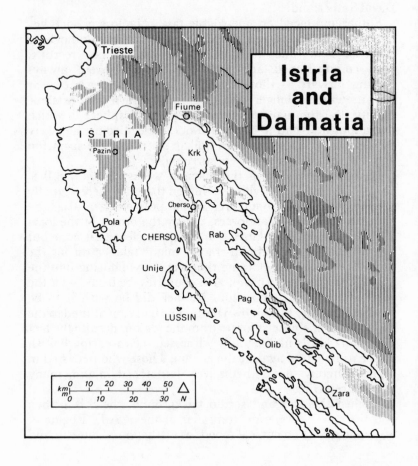

Surprise – the raider's most important advantage – was therefore almost impossible to achieve, and the recent pattern of large-scale deployment of S.B.S. men against strongly defended positions in what almost amounted to frontal attacks, had to be repeated. These attacks, though they would seem to have triggered a spate of desertions by yet more disillusioned Italian troops, were rarely successes in S.B.S. terms.

On the island of Lussin, for instance, the Villa Punta, main billet for the German garrison, was cleared and wrecked and an unknown number of the inhabitants incapacitated to some degree – but the operation cost the lives of Jimmy Lees and Marine Kitchingman, both old and valued members of the squadron, and Lieutenant Jones-Parry was badly wounded as were seven others. Moreover, an attempt to destroy the bridge linking Lussin with the neighbouring island of Cherso had to be abandoned, for the defenders were ready and waiting and determined to remain where they were – underlining a basic principle for raiding troops, that they should not be employed against specific, static or prepared targets.

This was an aspect of which Sutherland had always been extremely conscious, and with the prospect of operations on the Adriatic islands yielding ever-decreasing returns and with the recent spectacular advance of Patterson's squadron in Greece to encourage him, he decided to put a squadron ashore in Istria and perhaps score the same success in Fiume, Pola and Trieste as Patterson had gained in Athens.

He was defeated by the same political machination as that experienced by Lassen. The Yugoslav 45th Partisan Division had occupied the central areas of Istria for some time, extracting food and supplies from the local populace by force or threat; they had been left alone by the Germans in the area since they constituted no immediate menace and were as uninterested in genuinely liberating the area from the Axis forces as had been their opposite numbers in Salonika. The Partisans here had, in fact, no interest in any objective other than occupation first of the eastern half of the peninsula as the Germans withdrew, and then, most important of all, seizure of the port of Trieste – perhaps even at the cost of some casualties – before the British or Americans could get there from northern Italy to organise free elections.

In the meantime, however, the Partisans wished to continue living off the land, consoling the natives for their sacrifices with the thought that they were at least feeding their liberators. Now, suddenly, other liberators were arriving on the scene – liberators who wished and actually intended to attack the Axis forces and thus give perhaps a more convincing picture of a liberating force, and who had brought with them not only their own food and stores but also some extra for the indigenous population.

Unfortunately, in Istria the Partisan leaders held the trump cards, for there is little that one squadron of lightly armed raiding troops can do against the wishes of men who have an entire division at their disposal, even one armed and equipped more for policing civilians than fighting against enemy troops – especially when the motives of those leaders are not appreciated at first even in the field, let alone back at headquarters.

At first the Partisan leadership acted with restraint, good manners and an attempt at reasonableness. They had had no warning of the arrival of Sutherland and his men, they announced, all of whom were most welcome; but before they could be allowed to come ashore or more importantly to move inland, orders must be received from Belgrade.

The orders never came, of course, and Sutherland's increasing insistence upon his own duty to get his men into action against the common foe was parried with decreasing sympathy, until feigned ignorance and deliberate obstruction met his every request for co-operation. In the end a 'most offensive youth arrived with orders that we must pack up and leave forthwith. In his manner, bearing, and general obtuseness he strongly resembled a young Nazi!' – and although Sutherland rejected the stripling's demands and, realising at last that gross advantage was being taken of his patience, began preparations for attacking a railway-line, higher politics now intervened.

Discussions had taken place in Athens, in Belgrade, in Cairo – and for the moment Tito's stock was so high that his representatives won the day. Even as two S.B.S. patrols were loading up to set off into the interior despite Partisan intransigence, orders arrived for the whole squadron to be withdrawn – without having fired a shot against the German forces still in occupation of Istria.

At least the last wartime S.B.S. Mediterranean operation was

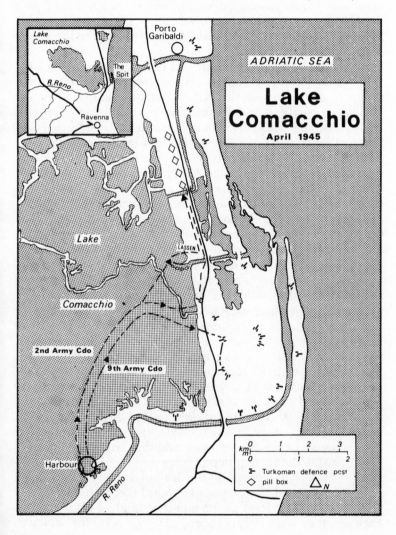

waterborne, and untrammelled by politics.

The Eighth Army had spent the winter of 1945 in conditions of excruciating discomfort in the Lower Romagna, a dull, flat, waterlogged breeding-ground for mosquitoes which reaches up from Rimini in the coastal curve to Venice, and inland to Ferrara and Padua. Its lowest and most dismal area constitutes Lake Comacchio, not so much a lake as a flooded area caused by a sand-ridge along the coastline holding back the collected surface water of an area the size of Northern Ireland.

Five miles across at its waist and nearly twenty miles long, Comacchio in the spring of 1945 blocked the northward progress of V Corps on the eastern flank of the Eighth Army. The lake's northern and western shores were held by German troops, and the sand-ridge to the east was blocked by defences manned by soldiers of a Turkoman division, who might have been uncertain as to where their loyalties lay but who could be depended upon to fight like furies once battle was joined. Their defences along the spit of sand were well sited and surrounded with mines, and V Corps patrols had quickly discovered that the Turkomans remained awake and alert during even the coldest nights.

Two marine and two army commandos held the V Corps coastal positions, briefed for an assault to by-pass the defences on the sand-ridge by pincer movements, one along the line of the eastern shore and the other across Comacchio. The problem for the latter exercise, however, was that it called for the use of deep-water channels, and no one knew where these might run – firstly because pre-war authorities had never felt it worthwhile to chart the lake, and secondly because even if they had, the channels changed course with every season. All that was known was that for large areas of the lake only six inches of water covered the soft, stinking mud at the bottom; that the water was deeper out in the middle around the few tiny shrub-covered islands which, it was strongly suspected, were used by the enemy as observation points; and that twenty-four inches was probably the average depth.

Twenty-four inches is also the draft of a Goatley float laden with ten men and their equipment, and the draft of a Carley float is very little less; as for powered landing-craft such as Fantails, they were rightly judged to be too noisy for what was likely to prove a lengthy approach to a hostile shore.

No approach at all could be made unless and until wide channels at least two feet deep had been found and charted – so during the cold, dismal nights of March, Lassen and his patrols were out from dusk to just before dawn, paddling their folboats through the rushes close up against the dimly seen islands, prodding the ooze below them with measuring sticks and on rare occasions dropping over the side a lead-weighted line. It was slow, bitterly cold work, but as the nights passed, the blank spaces on the wall-maps filled up, and to the relief of Brigadier R.J.F. Tod, it became evident that sufficient wide channels did in fact exist for the men of 2nd and 9th Army Commandos to make the sweep across the south-east corner of the lake and go ashore behind the first belt of defences.

Nevertheless on a night which would be especially chosen for its darkness, the chances of assault-craft veering off the channel and getting stuck in mud were obviously high, and the solution would be for the men who had charted the channels to lead the assault along them. On the night of April 1st/2nd, therefore, the folboats slid into the water and the pairs went out to await the dark bulk of the commando-craft closing up behind them, while, incredibly but ingeniously, loudspeakers behind them roared out the strains of Wagner's *Ride of the Valkyries* and the *Lohengrin Preludes* – as they had done day and night for a week – to drown the noises of preparation.

The S.B.S. patrols had a long time to wait. The vehicles bringing the commandos and their assault-craft bogged down in the approaches to the shoreline; the heavy boats themselves had to be dragged across 1,500 yards of glutinous, stinking mud before reaching water; and then the men they were supposed to carry had to cast around to find the mouths of the channels in which they and their craft could float. It was nearly 0430 before the whole force, with Lassen and his men guiding them, set out on the dark crossing – and as dawn paled the sky, a smoke screen made the S.B.S. task that much more difficult, though it undoubtedly helped the assault.

Both commandos landed successfully, and Lassen then led his men away to the north where they had been instructed to create a diversion – which they did by themselves landing and attacking machine-gun posts set in echelon along the narrow roadway threading the spit. Quite soon Trooper Crouch was killed, Shaun O'Reilly severely wounded and the rest pinned down – except for Andy Lassen himself, who, indifferent to the fire pouring down the line of the road, raced to the first pillbox and silenced it with grenades. He then used it as cover to shoot through the slit of the next pillbox which he then approached and put completely out of action with more grenades, repeating the process with the third and fourth pillboxes along the road.

By now, other men of the patrol had come up behind him – and a white cloth hung from the doorway of the fifth pillbox. However, as Lassen approached to take its surrender, he was shot from inside by men who quickly paid the price of their duplicity at the hands of Lassen's men.

Lassen himself was still alive when they had finished, and they tried to carry him back – but soon they came under heavy fire and were again pinned down, and during this time, Lassen died.

He was just twenty-five years old, had already won the Military Cross three times, and a few weeks later it was announced in London that he had been awarded a posthumous Victoria Cross. One had already been awarded for an act of bravery during the fighting on the Comacchio spit during those few, desperate hours – to Corporal Hunter of the Royal Marines – and it is unusual for two Crosses to be awarded for the same action; it is even more unusual for a holder of a foreign nationality to be awarded this highest of British awards. And Major Anders Lassen was a Dane from birth to death.

The war in Europe had now almost run its course. Bimrose and Stellin between them rallied the men of M Squadron as news of Lassen's death spread (it was over a week before the fact was finally accepted back at base), and M Squadron patrols remained on the miserable Comacchio islands until the middle of April. But then on the 18th the Eighth Army broke out through the Argenta Gap, the Germans began their last retreat towards the Austrian border, and on the 29th was signed the unconditional surrender of the remaining enemy formations in Italy.

There were for a few days plans and rumours that all

available S.B.S. officers and men would be dropped into Austria itself (it was not a suggestion which met with much enthusiasm at that stage of the war), but events were now moving too quickly. Even as Milner-Barry began the organisation and collection of the patrols still in the Dalmatians and Istria, Hitler committed suicide and a week later the final unconditional surrender of the German Wehrmacht was signed.

Perhaps it is fitting that the end of the Mediterranean operations of the Special Boat Squadrons should follow so quickly after the death of their most brilliant operator, for there seems no argument but that Anders Lassen was the embodiment of all they stood for – strength of purpose, imagination, flair, expertise and, perhaps most important of all, a light-hearted humour.

As David Sutherland, who has undoubtedly more right than anyone else to express an opinion on the subject, later wrote, 'I do not expect to see his like again.'

EPILOGUE

With the end of the war in Europe came first of all withdrawal from the various fronts upon which the squadrons had found themselves, a certain amount of regrouping and reconstitution, then a brief period of retraining for service in the Far East, quickly curtailed – to the immense relief of many who had not looked forward to participating in jungle work behind Japanese lines – by the dropping of atomic bombs on Hiroshima and Nagasaki. Parties ensued, reserves of back pay evaporated, and many Lugers, Birettas and Schmeissers were flogged to depot personnel who wished to present to those back home evidence of a more active role in the defeat of the Axis powers than they had in fact played. And all awaited return to pre-war life with happy expectancy.

It was then that the men of the Special Boat Squadrons – and indeed, of all such unorthodox and purely wartime formations – came up against an unforeseen inconvenience, leading in some cases to much unpleasantness. As none of these formations had existed before 1939, they had no peacetime bases – no barracks, no drill halls, no parade grounds upon which regimental ancestors had marched and countermarched behind regimental bands and been inspected by royalty of higher or lower degree; no messes hung with portraits of long-departed colonels, no tables laden with silver trophies of battles fought in previous centuries. Special Forces had, in fact, no 'depots' from which – and this was the crux of the matter for the majority of their personnel – they could be demobilised back to civilian life.

The answer to the problem was administratively simple, but in more human terms often unpleasant and to some degree painful. The special formations simply disintegrated – dissolved into their individual components who then returned to their original formations as privates, gunners, riflemen, marines, sappers, guardsmen or troopers – or their commissioned equivalents. In view of the fact that the majority wished anyway to return to civilian life, such a dissolution of wartime ties might now seem so inevitable as to be easily acceptable; but for the Special Forces this dissolution had to occur that much earlier, and the place of wartime friendships was taken not by the excitements of homecoming to family and friends, but by the disciplines and discomforts of a different type of military life to that to which they had lately been accustomed – in many cases those very disciplines and discomforts which had prompted the move to the unorthodox formation in the first place.

Although in most cases the passage through their parent formation's depot was not unduly protracted, for a large number it was disagreeable. No matter how distinguished their careers or however many ribbons they might be wearing on their chests, they often found themselves greeted with suspicion and sometimes with downright hostility. Long-forgotten nominal rolls were dug out and ostentatiously examined, and even when grudging admission was made that the returnees were not actually deserters from the British Army and thus ripe for consignment to military prisons, it was made obvious that they were considered to have abandoned their rightful duty to their regiments for service with disreputable bands of brigands. They could thus hardly expect to retain such rank or distinction as they had achieved now that they wished to return to respectability, were dropped with unwonted rapidity to what was called their 'war substantive' ranks, and many found themselves employed right up to their day of demobilisation upon the more dreary and monotonous of the innumerable tasks which depot personnel can always find for those they regard with disfavour.

But not even Purgatory lasts for ever, and eventually the day came for the majority to pass with varying degrees of relief and excitement through those vast hangars stocked with shirts, underclothes, socks and ties (of a variety of almost psychedelic patterns), then proceed to the section in which hung racks of suits attended by short, portly gentlemen with tape measures around their shoulders, who would hint at the existence of a better selection for those who looked gullible enough to pay for the privilege of being shown it. Then, with their new possessions packed into large cardboard boxes, they could proceed homeward and face, once the 'Demob pay and gratuity' had run out, the different strains and difficulties of civilian life.

For most those strains and difficulties were easily borne and overcome. Post-war shortages were nationwide and so more readily acceptable, and as the months passed, life became pleasanter – but by the same token the comforts of civilian life became for many tinged with monotony; soon memory was playing its tricks and investing the past with bluer skies and warmer climes than it had in reality possessed. Civilian clothes sat loosely and uncertainly on shoulders which had grown used after five years to the heavy masculinity of khaki serge or drill, and with the growing realisation that political friends and allies of the wartime years were proving inimical in peace, came the possibility that wartime skills might be needed again. But how could they be assembled and organised?

This was a matter which by 1947 was receiving close examination in Whitehall. Despite conventional military objection to unorthodox formations, the successes achieved by the Long Range Desert Group and the Special Air and Boat Squadrons between 1941 and 1945 could not be ignored, and as it happened one of the leading exponents of Special Operations, Brigadier J.M. Calvert who had led one of Wingate's Chindit columns in Burma and later assumed command of the Special Air Service regiments, was in a position to do something about it. He was a member of a committee examining the part played by guerilla forces in the recent conflict, and, having presented an overwhelming case for their existence and uses, he then won the argument for their future potential. All that was now required was to build an organisation to encompass it, and then find a physical home for its establishment – and if for the moment Whitehall seemed unable to stomach the thought of incorporating irregular forces into regular establishments, then perhaps a solution might be found in the fact that all Special Forces had been formed from volunteers. Thus it came about that the pre-war Volunteer Territorial Army solved the problem.

The Artists Rifles had been formed in 1860 as a part of the volunteer movement approved by the Government in the face of an apparent danger of invasion by France, and by the time the scare had died down, the regiment was well established. In those Victorian days the popular image of the artist was that of a man of creativity and action, and the idea of joining such an organisation became very popular among both the wealthy and the artistic. By 1877, its establishment of eight companies had been oversubscribed, though it could still to a great extent claim that each company had an artistic specialisation such as landscape or portrait painting, architecture or authorship. One of its first colonels was Lord Leighton, while William Morris was a private, and already the gifts to the regiment by some of its wealthier members were creating a collection of table silver and regimental trophies to compete with some of the more fashionable regular units.

Many members of the regiment went to South Africa to fight the Boers as part of the City Imperial Volunteers, but it was not until 1914 that the Artists Rifles went abroad as a formation, and even then they found themselves quickly ordered into reserve where, although given the prestigious duty of guarding General Headquarters, they became, in fact, a pool of junior officers. In less than two weeks over 100 of their number became second lieutenants (at a time when the average life in the trenches for that rank was about three weeks), and the first two years the Artists spent in France were as a training formation, at first of potential officers and then, once their value had been appreciated by the authorities, of machine-gunners.

It was not until the last days of 1917 that an Artists Rifles battalion as such went into the line to fight a notable action at Marcoing, and later in the last year of the war they were caught up in both the great retreat in the face of Ludendorff's offensive and the advance towards the frontiers which ended to everyone's relief on November 11th. The Artists Rifles as such had therefore hardly been in the line enough to win many battle honours, but its members serving with other regiments had individually gained 8 Victoria Crosses and 891 Military Crosses, while 56 ex-Artists had won the Distinguished Service Order, 35 had won decorations in the various Air Arms and some had even been decorated before being commissioned.

They had thus – though by an unusual method – achieved a fighting record of which any regiment could be proud, so when in 1921 the spirit of the volunteer movement again emerged and the Territorial Army was slowly reforming, one of the first battalions to contain enough men to hold a parade was the Artists Rifles.

But as it grew and developed between the wars, there was now no doubt as to its role. It was an officer-producing regiment, and applicants for membership were well aware of this – the drill hall and messes in Duke's Road were spacious, extremely comfortable and even elegant, the 'Bisley Hut' was in fact a superbly equipped and commodious chalet alongside the shooting ranges, and one of the duties of the permanent staff was to ensure that at the annual summer camp there were adequate parking facilities for the automobiles ranging from Morris Eights to Rolls Royces, in which a large proportion of the regiment would arrive.

They went to camp in August 1939, returned just before the end of the month and were promptly 'embodied' on September 3rd and sent down to a camp at St. Mary's Bay, Dymchurch. But this was the last time they moved as a body, for within three months at least 500 of them had been commissioned into other regiments or corps, and for the rest of the war the Artists Rifles was the organisation which ran one of the Officer Cadet Training Units.

Thus it came about that in 1945 when the O.C.T.Us. lost their purpose, the Artists Rifles, like the S.A.S. and the S.B.S., dissolved – not, like the latter, because they had no establishment or premises but because they had no role, for any officers trained during the post-war years would be trained by regulars in the traditional Military Academies then at Sandhurst and Woolwich. Unlike other famous Territorial regiments – the Inns of Court who had fought as an armoured car regiment, the City of London Yeomanry and the Westminster Dragoons who had both fought in tanks – the Artists had no Second World War battle experience to bring into the post-war world; just its mess silver, its drill hall, its 'Bisley Hut' – and its traditions as a famous Territorial regiment.

It was purpose-made for Brigadier Calvert's intentions, and in this imperfect world it is slightly surprising that he brought the amalgamation off and that it proved so successful. The 21st S.A.S. (Artists) was formed in 1947, recruitment began immediately and by the summer of 1948 it was possible to send the formation partly to the commando training camp at Plasterdown in Devon, partly to Appledore. Many ex-wartime S.A.S. and S.B.S. men joined and underwent retraining courses in some of the more abstruse military arts, while new recruits to service were sent as soon as possible on parachute courses to the R.A.F. training wing at Upper Heyford.

Commanding the new regiment was Lieutenant-Colonel B.M. Franks, who had commanded the S.A.S. in Italy; second-in-command was Major L.E.O.T. Hart, who had been Brigade Major at S.A.S. headquarters during 1944 and 1945.

Two squadrons were formed initially, each of two troops, and with special reference to the subject of this book, there is no doubt that from the start B Squadron regarded themselves as the legitimate heirs of the S.B.S. tradition. The squadron was commanded by Ian Lapraik with Stewart Macbeth as second-in-command, their first troop commanders were Dickie Livingstone and David Clark, and in due course 'Wally' Hughes became squadron sergeant-major. Weekend training was often spent paddling folboats at night through the narrow streams and dykes around Pirbright, annual camps were spent at establishments bordering the sea such as Appledore and Llanbedr where, although long distances were marched and much ammunition and explosive was expended, much time was also spent on or in the water. And in 1949, close liaison was established with the Royal Navy.

As a result of this, one Friday evening the squadron went down to Portsmouth with the purpose of spending the weekend practising launching and landing techniques at night from one of the few landing-craft still in naval service, filling in the Saturday afternoon paddling their folboats across Spithead to the Isle of Wight. They were afforded the hospitality of the Royal Marines barracks at Eastney for the time they were there, and on the Sunday morning, Major Lapraik and some others of the squadron who had been paddling around Langstone Harbour most of the night, found themselves making their somewhat weary ways back across the sandy spit known for generations as Fort Cumberland.

As they turned the last corner before the haven of the mess, to which already the scent of eggs and bacon was irresistibly drawing them, they saw in front of them the semi-circular end of a Nissen hut, its doors open and sounds of sporadic activity issuing from inside. Through the doors could be seen the unmistakable shapes of more folboats, surfboards and the dull black deformities of empty wet suits. Above them was painted the legend '*1st S.B.S.*'

The Royal Marines had taken over.

Towards the end of the war, the officers and men of the Special Boat Squadrons had suffered increasingly from the attentions of newspaper correspondents, Jellicoe claiming at one time that there were few details of his private life left unrevealed, and Private Watler figuring on some dingy front page as 'The Man the Germans couldn't Hold!' The S.B.S. received mention in several of the spate of books on special operations which appeared in the immediate post-war years, and John Lodwick's splendid evocation *The Filibusters* appeared in 1947.

But after that date, the wartime existence of the Special Boat Squadrons faded rapidly from the public memory, while their post-war existence was known only to very few. The Special Air Service on the other hand were known about to a limited extent, in both Territorial and Regular forms, their emblems occasionally glimpsed on vehicle or beret; but the Royal Marines guarded the secret of their Special Boat Sections (now squadron again) jealously, and it was not until the Falklands Campaign that the initials S.B.S. attained the slightest degree of post-war publicity.

This is how both the Department of the Commandant General of the Royal Marines, and the Secretariat of Defence, want it. As a paragraph in a recent broadsheet issued by one of them states:

> Fortunately, and unlike the Special Air Service at Prince's Gate [*Author's note*: the Iranian Embassy affair] the Squadron has not so far been committed to an operation under the full gaze of the international press and, even after some coverage of their participation in the Falklands operation, few details of their organisation, techniques and operational employment have emerged to the public.

In view of the fact that the lives of extremely brave and expert men could be placed in jeopardy should the vital element of surprise be lost to them in any future emergency, this is undoubtedly a thoroughly justified policy, and the author was by no means surprised when all his applications for information upon post-war S.B.S. activities were turned down – with the utmost charm and politeness, but with an equally unyielding implacability.

Certain aspects of S.B.S. operations and techniques had leaked out into the popular press, he was told, and of course no bar would or could be placed upon his repeating them; but the operational integrity of the Special Boat Squadron was of such vital importance, that decisions had been taken at the highest level that no information should be officially released which might in any way impair it.

So ... from post-war newspaper reports, it seems that S.B.S. teams have undertaken operations in Borneo, in Egypt at the time of the Suez débâcle, in Malaya – and undoubtedly in South Georgia and the Falkland Islands. According to one of the fuller reports during the South Atlantic operations, S.B.S. men landed at various places on both East and West Falklands some sixteen days before the main force went ashore; indeed, it was on the basis of information supplied by an S.B.S. team that the final choice of San Carlos Bay as the landing-place was made.

It would therefore seem that in one aspect at least the traditional S.B.S. tasks of reconnaissance and observation are still the same. But one wonders how their techniques have developed.

Obviously, much more sophisticated equipment is in use today than in the wartime years – wet suits have replaced the grease-covered Long Johns worn by Wilson in Navarino harbour, radios that actually work and do not require the energies of several fit men to carry around must be available. Those weapons so beloved of film-makers – silenced pistols – are certainly present in today's arsenals, though whether the terms of the Geneva Convention will now allow their use by soldiers is unlikely; but there is always the fighting-knife which did the job efficiently between 1939 and 1945. Cameras have presumably taken the place of the waterproof sketch pads, and more effective explosives and more reliable fuses have replaced plastic and time-pencils.

But folboats still have to be paddled by hand if they are to be flexible enough to go in and out of a submarine hatch and silent enough to slide in to the water's edge – and though one wartime problem has now apparently been solved, to one appalled discoverer the solution strikes so spine-chilling a response as to be unacceptable to anyone but ... well, a member of the S.B.S.

In order to infiltrate a man on to a hostile coast, it is necessary to go in under the enemy radar screen, i.e., on or under the water. But submarines are big nowadays and cannot go in too close, and, as will be remembered from the accounts of the raids on Crete and Rhodes, confinement aboard one for any length of time reduces physical fitness and thus operational efficiency.

The solution, apparently, is HALO – High Altitude, Low Opening – whereby the soldier is dropped from several thousand feet into the ocean, well out of sight of land, and there picked up by submarine. The techniques of free fall parachuting are nowadays almost commonplace and need not surprise anyone; but the prospect of landing in, say, the Indian Ocean, with complete dependence upon the navigational efficiency of an airplane pilot who has just flown several hundred miles, and the navigator of a submarine which has now been at sea – and out of sight of land – for three weeks, must require a deep faith in one's fellow-professionals which excites admiration.

Even so, when questioned upon how he felt as he floated upon the surface of an empty sea and watched the minuscule dot of the aircraft from which he had just descended disappear over the horizon, one who had just taken part in such an exercise replied, feelingly, '....... lonely!'

He had on that occasion to wait for nearly three hours before his next traumatic experience – known laconically as the '*Jesus Christ!*' syndrome – when suddenly from almost underneath him, emerged the submarine itself which then proceeded to take him aboard.

The modern techniques of entering and leaving a submarine in such circumstances are very much part of the forbidden area of public knowledge, but some time later this particular young man found himself swimming on his back into the darkness, watching a waterproof bag on the end of a towline containing clothes and equipment bobbing about beyond his flippers, and finding his way by means of a compass strapped to his wrist – and another enormous degree of faith in his delivery system, and his own expertise.

He remained ashore for almost a week, avoided the attentions of men searching specifically for him, carried out a survey of the beach itself, including underwater gradients at selected points, the bearing surface of the beach along its length, details of an underwater runnel and a protruding spit including heights of tide and rates observed at its edge, and investigated the exits from the beach with regard to their practicability as routes for vehicles from jeeps to tanks.

At the end of his sojourn on the island – and without receiving any confirmatory signal that the submarine was awaiting him, which might have betrayed his presence to the enemy – he entered the water and swam out into the darkness, again towing behind him a bag, this time containing samples, records and every item he could find which might give away to an observant enemy the fact of his recent presence in their territory and his actions while there. Again he directed himself simply by compass-bearing as he swam on his back, and some hour or so after he had entered the water he switched on what he called his 'bongle' and was in due course picked up by the submarine. He was, he said, quite glad about this.

Evidently, nothing of the spirit which enlivened and drove men like Tug Wilson and Marine Hughes, like Dickie Livingstone or Ian Lapraik, Lord Jellicoe, David Sutherland, David Clark, Stewart Macbeth or Shaun O'Reilly ... or Andy Lassen or all the others whose formation's initials were S.B.S. all those years ago, has been lost in the embodiment into the Royal Marines.

They may not know each other when they pass in the street, but no matter how many years separate their birth dates, they are linked by a common courage, a common spirit of adventure, a common humour.

The country, indeed the whole Western Alliance, has reason to be grateful for their existence.

CHRONOLOGY OF EVENTS

1940

  November First raid on Lofoten Islands.

1941

  January 31st Layforce leaves Scotland for Middle East.

  June Roger Courtney and Special Boat Section join H.M.S. *Medway*.

  June 22nd Wilson and Hughes raid Italian west coast railway.

  October Keyes' raid on Rommel's H.Q.

  November 18th Opening day of *Operation Crusader*. Courtney returns to England, his place taken by Mike Kealy.

  December Wilson's attempt to scuttle Italian destroyers beaten by cold.

1942

  January Eighth Army reaches the Gulf of Sirte.

  March 20th/21st Stirling's raid on airfield and railway near Benghazi.

  March 28th/29th Attempted raid on Benghazi itself.

  May 23rd Second raid on Benghazi. Ritchie and Allott investigate beaches at Cape Ras el Tin.

  May 26th Ritchie and Allott arrive at Gazala

  May 27th Opening of Battle of Gazala.

  May-June Langton, Newby and Sutherland survey Syrian beaches.

  June 11th-21st Jellicoe's raid on Heraklion.

  July Duncan and Newby captured on Sicily.

  August Attack on Daba landing strip.

  September 4th-18th Sutherland's and Allott's raid on Rhodes.

September 13th *Operation Daffodil*, attack on Tobruk.

October 21st American generals landed on Algerian coast by Courtney and Livingstone.

October 23rd The Battle of Alamein opens.

November 4th Breakout of Eighth Army.

November 30th Livingstone and Weatherall operating against Italian coastal installations, ships and railway.
Both return to England soon afterwards.

1943

January 23rd Stirling captured near Gabes.

February-May Reorganisation of Raiding Forces.

June 23rd-July 12th Sutherland, Lamonby and Lassen on second and annual raid on Crete.

July 10th *Operation Husky*, the Allied invasion of Sicily.

July 24th Mussolini removed from power, replaced by Marshal Badoglio.

September 3rd Badoglio signs armistice with Allies.

September 9th Jellicoe parachutes onto Rhodes.

September 10th/11th Castelorizzo secured as S.B.S. base.

September 13th Cos occupied by Jellicoe's party.
Jellicoe investigates Leros defences.

September 14th Milner-Barry and Sutherland visit Kalymnos and Samos.
Sutherland arrives at Kalymnos to be joined later by Milner-Barry.
Lapraik visits Castelorizzo and Cos *en route* for Simi.
German programme of air attack launched on Cos.
Bulk of S.B.S. now on Kalymnos.
Lassen organises defences on Calchi.
L.R.D.G. move into the Aegean.

October 2nd Prendergast, Sutherland and Milner-Barry go to Leros for conference with Turnbull.
Enemy convoy sighted sailing N/E from Naxos.

October 3rd Germans re-take Cos.

October 4th-13th Milner-Barry mounts rescue operations on Cos.

October 7th Lapraik's first defence of Simi.

October 12th Lapraik withdraws from Simi to Castelorizzo.
Royal Navy suffers heavy losses in Aegean.

Keith Balsillie reconnoitres Patmos and neighbouring islands.
November 12th German invasion of Leros.
November 16th Leros surrendered, S.B.S. and L.R.D.G. escape to Lisso.
November 17th/18th Samos evacuated.
Lapraik's patrols make lightning attacks on Simi, Nisiros, Piscopi and again on Simi.
Lapraik's squadron withdraws to Haifa.

1944
January 31st Lassen returns to Calchi.
February-March Series of raids by L Squadron under Patterson, on Stampalia, Simi, Archi and Lisso.
March Sutherland's squadron under Milner-Barry and containing John Lodwick, return to Castelorizzo from the Lebanon.
April Lodwick's raid on Kalymnos.
Clarke visits Patmos, Lisso and Archi.
Balsillie on Piscopi.
Clarke's patrol on Amorgos and Nisiros.
Blythe betrayed and captured on Calchi.
April 22nd-24th Lodwick's raid on Mykonos.
April 22nd-29th Lassen's attack on Santorin.
April 25th Clarke surprises Germans on Ios.
April 28th Clarke takes garrison on Amorgos.
May Lassen's trip to Paros.
May 16th Clarke on Naxos.
Sutherland on Siphnos.
June Lees and Bury in northern Sporades.
Bimrose forced to land on Greek mainland.
Lees on Kalymnos.
Royal Marines destroy enemy shipping in Leros harbour.
July 13th Lapraik's major attack on Simi.
July 23rd Third annual raid on Crete. Lodwick taken prisoner.
August 27th Lassen's attack on enemy communications in Yugoslavia.
August-September McGonigal wrecks installations and ambushes German patrols in Yugoslavia.
September 23rd Patterson's men dropped on Araxos.
October 2nd/3rd Enemy withdraws from Patras.

October 7th Corinth and Sparta surrendered to Allies.

October 14th Athens liberated.

October 30th Patterson's squadron reach Yugoslav-Albanian border.

Lassen liberates Salonika.

December 3rd Lassen on Crete to accept German surrender.

Clynes killed and Bimrose wounded.

December 23rd Ian Patterson killed in plane crash.

December 8th-January 8th S.B.S. involved in Greek civil war.

1945

January-March S.B.S. and L.R.D.G. in Yugoslavia.

S.B.S. attacks on Dalmatian Islands.

March-April Sutherland and McGonigal's squadron in Istria.

April 1st/2nd S.B.S. lead Commandos across Lake Comacchio.

Lassen killed.

April 18th Eighth Army breakout through Argenta Gap.

April 29th Unconditional surrender of all German troops in Italy.

Hitler commits suicide.

May 7th Unconditional surrender of all German armed forces agreed at General Eisenhower's H.Q.

May 9th V.E. day.

NOTES

Crown copyright material throughout this book is reproduced by permission of the Controller of Her Majesty's Stationery Office.

Prologue

1. Crown copyright, from report 'The first operation of No. 2 S.B.S.' by Captain R.P. Livingstone, by permission of Mrs. Norah Livingstone.

Chapter 1. *Early Days, 1940 – September '42*

1. Crown copyright, from 'Report on patrol carried out on S/M Torbay 2-4-42 to 24-4-42' by Cpl. Booth.

2. Crown copyright, from 'Report of Folboat Operation in Combined Operation' by Lt. T.B. Langton, Irish Guards.

3. Crown copyright, from 'Report by Captain R.K.B. Allott, Special Boat Section, of Operation with L.R.D.G. on 20/21st March, 1942' and 'Report by Captain R.K.B. Allott, Special Boat Section, of Operation on 28/29th March, 1942, in the vicinity of Benghazi'.

4. Crown copyright, from 'Operation on Crete, dictated by Captain Lord Jellicoe, Coldstream Guards, 1 S.A.S. Regt., on 30th November, 1942', by permission of the Rt. Hon. Earl Jellicoe, D.S.O., M.C.

5. Crown copyright, from 'Report on Operation ANGLO', by Lt. D.G.C. Sutherland, The Black Watch, by permission of Colonel D.G.C. Sutherland, M.C.

6. Ibid.

7. Ibid.

Chapter 2. *Reorganisation, September '42 – July '43*

1. Crown copyright, from 'Cruise in H.M.S./M. Ursua!' by Captain R.P. Livingstone, by permission of Mrs. Norah Livingstone.

2. Ibid.

3. Ibid.

4. John Verney, *A Dinner of Herbs*, Collins, 1966.

5. Walter Milner-Barry, unpublished diary, by permission of the Executors of the Estate of the late Walter Milner-Barry, Esq., O.B.E.

Chapter 3. *Dodecanese Disaster, July '43 – November '43*

1. Crown copyright, from the report on the mission to Rhodes carried out on the night of September 9th, 1943 by Major Lord Jellicoe, and subsequent operations, by permission of the Rt. Hon. Earl Jellicoe, D.S.O., M.C.

2. Ibid.

3. Crown copyright, from 'Report on activities of S.B.S. under command of Major D.G.C. Sutherland in the Dodecanese between Oct. 1st and Dec. 1st 1943', by permission of Colonel D.G.C. Sutherland, M.C.

4. Crown copyright, from Order of the Day 'For the R.A.F.' October 5th, 1943 by Major J.N. Lapraik, D.S.O., M.C., by permission of Colonel J. Neilson Lapraik, D.S.O., O.B.E., M.C.

Chapter 4. *The Aegean Island Raids, November '43 – August '44*
1. Quoted in *The Filibusters* by John Lodwick, Methuen, 1947.
2. Ibid.
3. Crown copyright, from 'Operation Report No. 14, Mikonos' by Lt. J. Lodwick.
4. Ibid.
5. Crown copyright, from 'Operation Report No. 13 Thira' by Captain A. Lassen, M.C.
6. Ibid.
7. Quoted in *The Filibusters* by John Lodwick, Methuen, 1947.
8. Walter Milner-Barry, unpublished diary, by permission of the Executors of the Estate of the late Walter Milner-Barry, Esq., O.B.E.
9. John Lodwick, *The Filibusters*, Methuen, 1947, with acknowledgements to the Executors of the Estate of the late John Lodwick, Esq.

Chapter 5. *Triumph and Frustration on the Mainland, August '44 – April '45*
1. Crown copyright, from 'Report on Operations in Yugoslavia, 27 August to 6 September, 1944' by Captain Anders Lassen, M.C.
2. John Lodwick, *The Filibusters*, Methuen, 1947, with acknowledgements to the Executors of the Estate of the late John Lodwick, Esq.
3. Walter Milner-Barry, unpublished diary, by permission of the Executors of the Estate of the late Walter Milner-Barry, Esq., O.B.E.
4. Crown copyright, from 'Report on Operation Towanbucket' by Lt. Col. Lord Jellicoe, by permission of the Rt. Hon. Earl Jellicoe, D.S.O., M.C.
5. Ibid.
6. John Lodwick, *The Filibusters*, Methuen, 1947, with acknowledgements to the Executors of the Estate of the late John Lodwick, Esq.
7. Crown copyright, from 'Report on Operation Towanbucket' by Lt. Col. Lord Jellicoe, by permission of the Rt. Hon. Earl Jellicoe, D.S.O., M.C.
8. Walter Milner-Barry, unpublished diary, by permission of the Executors of the Estate of the late Walter Milner-Barry, Esq., O.B.E.
9. Ibid.
10. Quoted in *The Filibusters* by John Lodwick, Methuen, 1947.
11. Walter Milner-Barry, unpublished diary, by permission of the Executors of the Estate of the late Walter Milner-Barry, Esq., O.B.E.
12. John Lodwick, *The Filibusters*, Methuen, 1947, with acknowledgements to the Executors of the Estate of the late John Lodwick, Esq.
13. Quoted in *The Filibusters* by John Lodwick, Methuen, 1947.

INDEX

Alamein, El, iii, 1, 25, 33-4, 46, 50, 86; 204
Alam Halfa, iii, 1
Alexandria, iii, 14, 20, 24, 25, 27, 32, 46, 107, 134
Algiers, ii, 1, 85, 166
Aliakmon, R., 168, 176
Alinda Bay, 95, 117-18
Allott, Capt. R.K.B. 'Tramp', "Rommel Raid" 17; 20, 21-3; investigates beaches at Cape Ras el Tin 23-4; on Crete 26, 34; on Rhodes 36-7, 40-2; taken prisoner 44-5; 203-4
Amorgos, 134, 136, 138-40; 205
Anderson, Lieut., on Stampalia 128; on Kalymnos 130
Anidhros, 136, 142
Antimachia, 95, 97, 99, 105-7
Apollonia, iii, 16
Apostolos, schooner, 66-8
Araxos, 166, 167-8, 170; 205
Arcangelo, Cape, 35, 43
Archi, 95, 128-9, 133, 137; 205
Asbery, Cpl, 128
Athens, iii, 13, 104, 135, 152, 165, 168; German withdrawal from 174-5; civil war 180-1; 182, 186; 206
Athlit, iii, 63, 66, 69, 70, 85, 100, 126

Badoglio, Marshal, 84, 92, 103; 204
Balsillie, Lieut. Keith, on Patmos 116; on Piscopi 133-4; on Santorin 142-3; 159; enters Piraeus 173; 205
Barce, iii, 25; raid on 46-7
Bardia, iii, 49
Bari, ii, 161, 166
Barr, Cpl, 20, 21, 26
Barrow, Mne, 34, 37-8, 45
Beda Littoria, iii, 16
Beirut, iii, 34, 44, 52, 68, 85, 88
Benghazi, ii, Stirling's raids on 21-3, 25; *Daffodil* 46; 203
Benina, ii, 22; *Daffodil* 46
Bergé, Commandant, 25, 28-32
Bimrose, Lieut. Charles, on Nisiros 124; arrested by guerillas on Greek mainland 147; *Manna* 167-8, 173; wounded on Crete 182; rallies M Squadron after Comacchio 190; 205-6

Bitter Lakes, iii, 13
Bir Hacheim, iii, 24
Bishop, Cpl, 112-13
Bizerta, ii, 1
Blythe, Capt. H.W., 135, 158; 205
Bodrum, 95, 137, 150
Bon, Cape, ii, 102
Booth, Cpl, 14, 20, 45
Buerat, ii, 21, 25
Bury, Lieut. 'Bob', on Simi 123-4; in N. Sporades 147; killed 181; 205

Cairo, iii, 13, 25, 27, 34, 45, 47, 60, 78-9, 81; re Italian Armistice 85-8; 91, 96, 98-9, 103, 113, 115, 120, 130, 135, 159, 186
Calambakidis, Sub-Lieut., 34, 37-8, 42-4
Calato, 34, 35, 36, 37-40, 43, 44, 87, 90, 105
Calchi, 95, 101, 127, 135, 158; 204-5
Calvert, Brig. J.M., 195, 197
Campioni, Adml, 88-93, 95, 104, 114
Cardamena, 95, 106
Carmel, Mt, iii, 63
Castelorizzo, 92, 93-4, 95, 96, 103, 105, 113, 137, 157; 204-5
Castelrosso, 93-4, 96-7, 98, 100, 102, 107, 108-9, 120, 126, 131-2
Casulli, Lieut. Stefan, on Cos 98; on Kalymnos 99; 116, 120; on Santorin 141-3; killed 143
Cattavia, 35, 90
Cherso, 184-5
Chevalier, Capt. Harold, 116, 120, 146, 159
Chios, iii, 100, 104, 136
Churchill, Winston S., 1, 13; re Fitzroy Maclean 59; 70; re Badoglio 84; re American air power over Aegean 114; recommends Greek landings 166
Clark, Lieut David, 125, 128-9; on Kalymnos 130; on Crete 164; in Greece 169-70, 175; 198, 202
Clark, Maj.-Gen. Mark (U.S.A.), N. African landings 5-8, 10, 52
Clarke, Capt. Kingsley Gordon 'Nobby', on Patmos 133; 134; on Ios 138-9; on Naxos 145-6; 158; 205
Clynes, Capt. Charles, on Simi 152-4;

killed 182; 206
Comacchio, Lake, 187, 188-90; 206
Corinth, 168, 172-4; 204
Cos, iii, 95, 97-100, 104-10, 115, 116,
    125-6; 147-8, 157; 204
Costi, Lieut., 27, 29-32
Courtney, Capt. C.B. 'Gruff', N. African
    landings 3-10; 11, 52; 204
Courtney, Capt. Roger 'Jumbo', 11-12,
    14, 19, 45, 51, 149; 203
Coxon, Lieut.-Col., 174, 176
Crete, iii, 14, 25-32, 70, 71, 74, 80, 104,
    115, 136, 164-5, 181; 204-6
Cyprus, iii, 66-7, 88, 92, 93, 94, 96, 99-
    100, 105, 157
Cyrene, iii, 16

Daba, iii, 32; 203
Darrell, Cpl Porter (U.S.A.), 112-13, 132
Dereman, Port, 127, 137, 157
Derna, iii, 25
Dolbey, Maj., 89-92
Duggan, Mne, 34, 37-44
Duncan, Capt. George, 20, 21, 26, 33,
    45; 203

Elia, Mt, 35, 36, 41
Euboea, 136, 168, 175

Fanetza, Col., 92, 94-6, 98
Feeberry, Cpl (later Sgt), 18-19, 51
Fiume, ii, 184, 185
Florina, 168, 176-7
Foca, Cape, 95, 105
Foot, Lieut. Jimmy, 6-7, 9-10, 52
Franks, Lieut.-Col. B.M., 198

Gabes, ii, 61; 204
Gaza, iii, 87
Gazala, iii, 21, 24; 203
Geary, Sgt R. 'Tanky', 123-4
Genoa, Gulf of, ii, 52
Grant, Donald (U.S.A.), 134
Greaves, Cpl S., 75, 77, 80, 112-13
Greek Sacred Squadron, 52, 61, 66, 139,
    148, 152, 155-9, 177
Gray, Capt., 169-70
Gruda, ii, 162
Gumushluk, 95, 116, 137
Gurna Bay, 95, 117

Haifa, iii, 63, 67, 88, 93, 100, 120, 124,
    157, 183; 205
Hamblen, Col. (U.S.A.), 7-9
Harden Lieut. Dick, 130
Harris, Mne, 34, 37-8, 45, 143
Haselden, Lieut.-Col. John, 45-8; killed
    49
Henderson, Sgt B.B. 'Brown Body', 51,
    132, 141-2, 144, 159
Henshaw, Liet. J.C., 162, 181
Heraklion, iii, 25-7, 31-2, 70-2, 74, 79,
    181-2; 203
Himeimat, iii, 49
Holmes, Col. Julius C. (U.S.A.), 4, 7
Holmes, L.-Cpl R., 73-4, 134, 138
Horner, Cpl, 150-1
Hughes, Mne Wally (later S.S.M.), first
    S.B.S. raid 11; 12, 14, 15-16, 20, 51;
    on Piscopi 134; on Santorin 142-3;
    149, 159, 198, 202; 203

Iannadi, 35, 102
Icaria, 104, 136
Ios, 36, 138-40; 205
Istria, ii, 165, 184, 185-7, 191

Jalo, iii, 46
Jellicoe, Capt. The Right Hon. Earl
    George (later Maj.), 25; on Crete 27-
    32; commands re-formed S.B.S.
    squadron, 63-5; at Cairo briefing 85-
    8; on Rhodes 88-94; 95-6; on Cos 97;
    on Leros 98-9; 100, 103, 109; on
    Leros 117-19; 120, 126, 131, 163,
    165; plans for *Towanbucket* 167, 169;
    takes Patras 170-2; cycles into
    Athens 174-5; promoted to Lieut.-
    Col., leaves S.B.S. 183; 199, 202;
    203-4
Jewell, Lieut. N.L.A. 'Bill', (R.N.), 3, 5,
    8
Jones, Gnr, 76-8

Kabrit, iii, 30, 50, 62
Kahane, Cpl, 142-3
Kalamata, 167-8
Kalymnos, 95, 99-100, 102-3, 105-7, 130,
    132, 137, 148, 150; 204-5
Karlovossi, 99, 137
Kasos, 104, 137
Kastelli, 25-6, 70-1, 74, 79
Katakolon, 168, 169
Kealy, Capt. Mike, replaces Courtney in
    command 19; 25-6; returns to U.K.
    45, 51; 203
Kesterton, Sgt, 89-90, 92, 94, 97
Keyes, Lieut.-Col. Geoffrey, 16, 18;
    killed 19; 203
Kleman, Gnl-Mjr von, 90-2, 104, 112
Kokinoxos, Cape, 26, 70, 71, 81
Kozani, 168, 176-7
Krk, 184
Krotos, 26, 31-2
Kuffra, iii, 50
Kythira, iii, 104, 147, 168

Laigueglia, ii, 54
Laki, Port, 95, 102, 119
Lamia, 168, 175-6
Lamonby, Lieut. Keith, 52, 63; second Crete raid 70-4, 78-81; killed 81; 204
Langton, Lieut. T.B. 'Tommy', 17-18, 33; *Daffodil* 47-50, 52; 59; commands L Detachment 63, 85; 203
Lapraik, Maj. J. Neilson 'Ian', commands M Detachment 86, 88, · 100-2, 104, 109-13, 120, 123-4, 146-8; main raid on Simi 152-4, 155; with Greek Sacred Squadron 159, 177; 198, 202; 204-5
Lardo, 35, 102
Larissa, 168, 176
Lassen, Capt. Anders (later Maj.), 68-9; second raid on Crete 70-1, 74-81; on Simi 100-1, 104, 110-13; on Calchi 127; on Santorin 141-5; 147, 158; in Yugoslavia 162-3; commands M Squadron 177; liberates Salonika 178-80; 181-2; Lake Comacchio 189; killed 190-1; 202; 204-6
Laycock, Lieut.-Col. Robert, 12; formed Layforce 13, 19; 69
Lees, Lieut. Jimmy, 147, 148; killed 185; 205
Lemnitzer, Brig.-Gen. (U.S.A.), 6,9,10.
Lemnos, iii, 104
Leros, 95, 98, 102, 104, 109, 115; main fight for 116-20, 123; 137, 149-50; 204-5
Lindos, 35, 41, 87
Lisso, 95, 120, 128-9, 133, 137; 205
Livingstone, Capt. R.P. 'Dickie', N. African landings 4-10; attack on Italian railway 52-7; returns to U.K. 58; 131, 198, 202; 204
Lloyd-Owen, Capt. David, 102
Lodwick, Capt. John, 131-2; on Kalymnos 133; on Mykonos 139-41; 157; on Crete 165; 170, 177, 199; 205
Lussin, 184-5

Macbeth, Capt. J.S.F. 'Stewart', 88, 94; on Cos 97, 99; on Simi 111; 125, 131, 147; on Kalymnos 148; main raid on Simi 152-3; re Patterson's death 182; 198, 202
Maclean, Capt. Fitzroy (later Brig.), in Benghazi 23; 59-61; commands M Detachment 63-4; in Yugoslav mountains 85-6; 88
Magnus, *Kapitan Zur Zee*, 169-71
Maidstone, H.M.S., 52, 58
Maleme, 25-6, 181
Malona, 35, 36-7
Malta, ii, 25, 85, 86, 105, 115
Marguerite II, S.S., 57-8

Marizza, 34, 35, 37, 44, 87, 90-1, 105, 137
Marmari, 95, 99
Mascherpa, Adml, 98-9
Massari, 35, 36-7
Matruh, iii, 81
Mayne, Capt. R.B. 'Paddy', 61-2
McGonigal, Lieut. Ambrose, 163-4; 205-6
Medway, H.M.S., 14; 203
Megara, 168, 173-4
Mele, Cape, ii, 53
Meravigli, 136, 142-3
Mesara, 26, 30
Milner-Barry, Capt. Walter (later Maj.), 66-7; on Rhodes 88; 94; on Cos 97; 99-100, 102, 103; on Kalymnos 106-7; 131, 156, 159; in Italy 161; commands H.Q. Squadron 165, 167; in Greece 169-75; 191; 204-5
Mitford, Capt. Bruce, 128-9
Molo Point, 123, 151, 153
Mussolini, Benito, 83-4; 204
Mykonos, 136, 138-41; 205
Mytilene, iii, 104

Navarino Bay, iii, 15
Naxos, 103, 136, 146; 204-5
Newby, Lieut. Eric, 20, 33, 45, 59, 131; 203
Nicholson, Sgt Jack, 75-7, 80, 141-4, 145
Nisiros, 95, 124, 131, 134, 158; 205

Olib, 184
Oneglia, ii, 57
Operation(s) *Albumen*, 70-81; *Daffodil*, 46-9, 51; 204; *Husky*, 83; 204; *Manna* 166-73; *Towanbucket*, 167
O'Reilly, Cpl Shaun, 51, 66-7, 100, 113, 127, 142, 144, 158, 163; wounded 190; 202

Pag, 184
Panormiti, 111, 123, 151
Pantellaria, ii, 13
Papanikolis, H. Hellenic M Sub, 34
Paros, 136, 145; 205
Partheni Bay, 95, 117, 120
Patmos, 95, 116, 128-9, 133, 136; 205
Patras, iii, 167, 168, 169-73, 174; 206
Patterson, Maj. Ian, 125-7; commands L Squadron 131; in Italy 164, 168-77; death 182; 205-6
Penzik Bay, 137, 150, 157
Pethi Bay, 110-11, 151
Peza, 71, 72
Pickney, Capt. Philip, 65, 69
Piscopi, 95, 124, 133, 137; 205
Piraeus, 168, 172-3, 175

Pomford, Cpl, 20, 22, 51, 138
Pola, ii, 184, 185
Prendergast, Lieut.-Col. Guy, 102; 204

Qattara Depression, iii, 25, 50

Rab, 184
Rachi Ridge, 95, 117-18
Ramseyer, Lieut.-Com. Frank, 88, 103, 120, 154
Ras el Tin, Cape, iii, 23; 203
Rethimnon, 26, 182
Rhodes, iii, 13; attack on 34-43; 87-8, 92-4, 95-7, 101-2, 103, 104-5, 137; 204
Riley, Cpl John (later S.-S.M.), 20, 51, 158
Ritchie, Lieut. Duncan (R.N.), 23-4; 203
Rommel, *Generalfeldmarschall* Erwin, 1, 16-17, 24, 33-4
Rowe, Lieut. R.G., 70, 72, 78-81

St Angelo, Monte, ii, 161
St Michael Monastery, 151, 152
Salonika, iii, 103, 109, 163, 165, 168, 178-81, 185; 206
Samos, 99-100, 104, 115, 120-1, 126, 137, 146; 204-5
Santorin, 136, 138, 141-2; 205
Savvas, Nicolas, 34, 37, 38, 40
Scarpanto, iii, 109, 115, 137
School Hill, 112, 151
Sciathos, 168, 177
Seraph, H.M. Sub, 2-5, 8, 10
Sikh, H.M.S., 46, 49
Simi, 92, 94, 95-6, 100-3, 104, 109, 111-13, 123-4, 128-9, 137, 149; main attack on 151-5; 204-5
Sinclair, Cpl, 22-3
Siphnos, 136, 146; 205
Sirte, Gulf of, ii, 21; 203
Skopelos, 168, 177
Solomon, Lieut. Martin, 177-8
'Sponge Queen', The, 99-100, 107
Stampalia, 95, 102, 104, 128, 132, 136; 205
Stellin, Capt. D.J. 'Stud', 86, 101, 153, 155, 190

Stimson, H.L. (U.S.A.), 114-15, 166
Stirling, Maj. David, 20; Benghazi raids 21-3; 25, 51, 58-9; *Daffodil* 46-7; 51-2, 59; captured 61-2; 203-4
Suda Bay, 26, 181
Sutherland, Lieut, David G.C. (later Lieut.-Col.), 20, 23; first raid on Crete 26, 32; 33-4; on Rhodes 36-44; 45, 51-2, 59, 60; commands S Detachment 63, 69; second raid on Crete 70-1, 78-82; 88, 93, 95, 97, 99, 100, 102, 105-6, 109, 116, 120, 131, 135, 138, 145-6, 158-9; in Italy 161; 177; commands S.B.S. 183; in Yugoslavia 185-6; 191, 202; 203-6
Syracuse, ii, 84

Tabarca, ii, 62
Tenez, Cape, ii, 2
Tewfik, schooner 157-8
Tobruk, iii, 17, 24; *Daffodil*, 45-9, 50; 204
Torbay, H.M. Sub, 14, 17
Traveller, H.M. Sub, 43-4
Trieste, ii, 184-5
Tsigantes, Col., 66
Tsoucas, Capt., 34, 40, 41-4
Tuckey, Sub.-Lieut., 135
Turnbull, Col. D., 87, 92, 94-6, 98, 102, 148; on Simi 152-3; 204
Tymbaki, 25, 26, 70, 71, 72, 79

Ursula, H.M. Sub, 52-4, 56-8

Verney, Capt. John, 63, 65, 85, 131
Volos, 168, 177-8

Watler, Pte R., 49, 66, 106-8, 199
Weatherall, Sgt J., 52-7, 58; 204
Webb, L.-Cpl, 12
Wilson, Lieut.-Gen. H. Maitland, 59-61, 89, 115
Wilson, Lieut. 'Tug', 11, 12, 14, 15-16, 19, 45, 202; 203
Wynne, Sqd.-Ldr, 169, 171

Yedi Atalla, 137, 148, 156

Zara, ii, 183, 184
Zulu, H.M.S., 46, 49